The Truth About the Neutron Bomb

The Truth About the Neutron Bomb

THE INVENTOR OF THE BOMB SPEAKS OUT

Sam Cohen

WILLIAM MORROW AND COMPANY, INC.
NEW YORK 1983

Library of Congress Cataloging in Publication Data

Cohen, S. T.
The truth about the neutron bomb.

1. Neutron bomb. 2. Atomic warfare—Moral
and ethical aspects. 3. United States—Military
policy. 4. Cohen, S. T. I. Title.
UC1282.N48C64 1983 355.8′2 82-14239
ISBN 0-688-01646-4

Printed in the United States of America

First Edition

1 2 3 4 5 6 7 8 9 10

Book Design by Patty Lowy

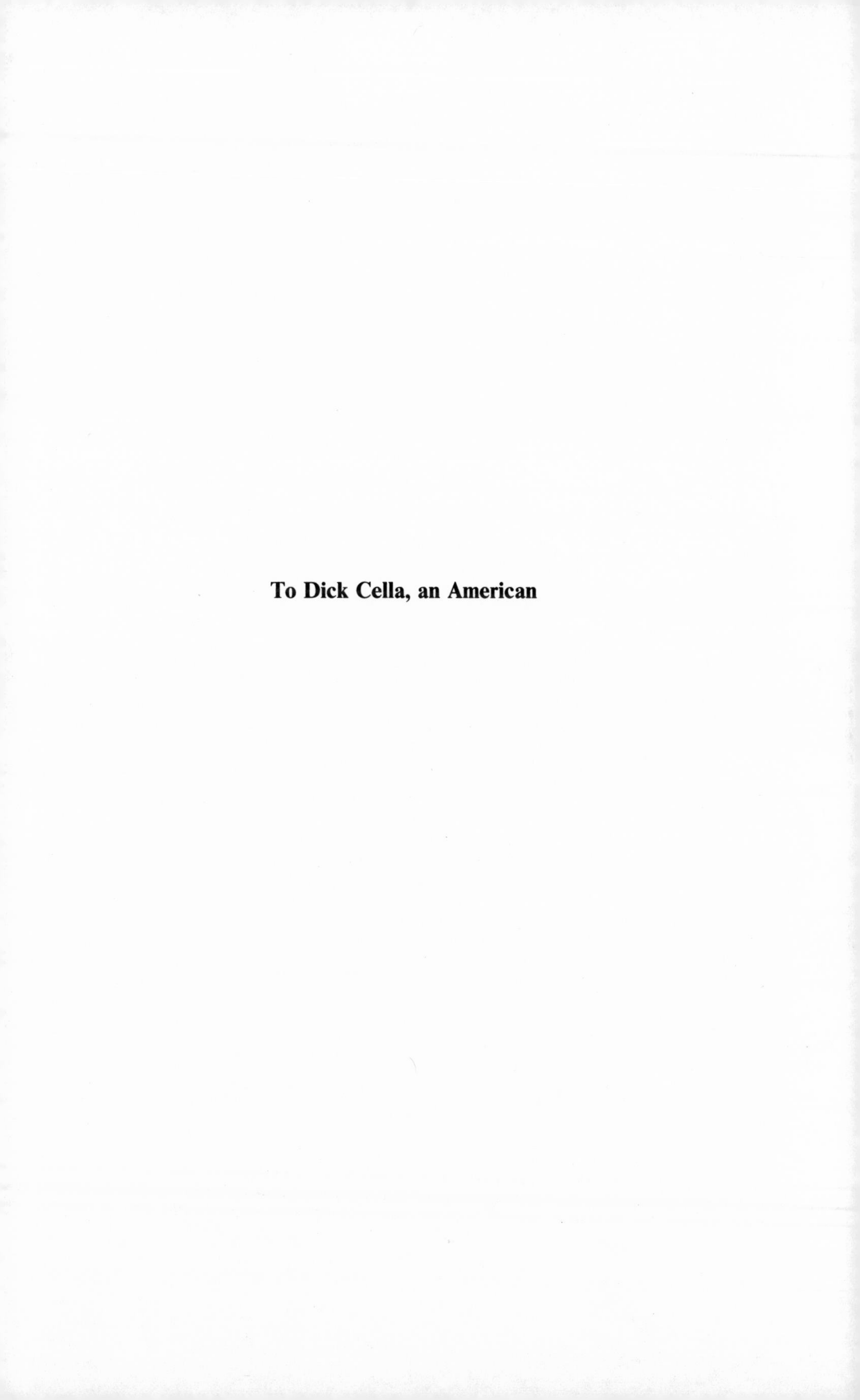

To Dick Cella, an American

ACKNOWLEDGMENTS

Many thanks are due to those who have helped and encouraged me in this effort.

My dear wife Margaret displayed great faith and tolerance in allowing my writing to take priority over my household duties for many weeks. It was my daughter Carla who first read what I wrote and told me I really had something going and to push hard on it. Another family member, our poodle Virgie, graciously forsook the attention I normally give to her and loyally sat by me as I wrote.

My friend Joe Angell was a godsend in helping me get the show on the road, and my friend Larry Beilenson, who has had a profound effect on my thoughts on war and peace, was in no small way responsible for my decision to sit down and write. And my friends Betty Baxter and Glenda Watson were selfless and indispensable in helping me get out the manuscript.

Finally, there are my editors Bruce Lee and Kristina Lindbergh. They were a pleasure to work with; their abilities are simply splendid; I hope they are willing to work with me again.

CONTENTS

INTRODUCTION

As I RECALL IT, I was doing my daily exercises in front of the television and watching the news to relieve the boredom of hefting dumbbells. The program was interrupted that August 8, 1981, for an announcement from Santa Barbara that the President had authorized the production of neutron warheads. Almost immediately, before I could begin to contemplate what the announcement meant, and what might happen to me as a result, the phone rang. It was my old friend Jess, who had been watching the same program. "Congratulations," he said, "your bomb finally made it."

"Sounds like it," I replied, "but what difference is it going to make?"

Jess, who had been working professionally on nuclear weapons matters for nearly thirty years, had no answer.

The decision to build the neutron bomb, as profound as it may seem, was really of precious little significance. The purported role of the weapon, at least as it has been heralded by the U.S. government and echoed by those who remain loyal to government national security policies, is to hold back an avalanche of Russian tanks, which, because there are no neutron weapons in Western Europe's arsenal, would otherwise overwhelm NATO's inadequate conventional defenses.

The truth of the matter is to the contrary. For, as I will explain in detail later in this book, if we deployed neutron weapons to Europe, we would be deploying weapons we don't know how to use, which the Europeans don't want us to use and which the Soviets won't let us use—because they'll use their nuclear weapons first to make sure we *can't* use ours.

Nearly a quarter of a century ago another friend of mine, Jack Morse, a dedicated and helpful ally in fighting the first neutron bomb crusade, told me that the neutron bomb represented an idea whose time had not yet come, but would. At best, he was half right. President Reagan *has* made the decision to produce the bomb. However, if we consider that it's taken twenty-five years for this time to come—and how much the world has changed in the meantime—and that the President's decision still will not succeed in deploying neutron weapons with a credible doctrine for their use, then I would say that the time has come too late—far too late.

The neutron bomb symbolizes the futility of U.S. involvement in NATO. It is not a means of salvation that will help end the problems that NATO faces. That hope is a myth that has been created by political propaganda. In fact, considering the violent political opposition in Europe to the idea of our deploying the neutron bomb, and our deference to this opposition, the story of the neutron bomb proves, more clearly than ever, that we cannot defend Europe.

I'll go one step further. America cannot solve the problems of defending Europe with nuclear weapons, including neutron bombs. Why? Because the Europeans are not truly concerned about defending themselves. They will not think seriously about nuclear weapons until America withdraws its troops and nuclear weapons from NATO and we force them to consider how they should defend themselves. Furthermore, we are unable to use nuclear weapons in Asian wars to contain Soviet aggression. And keep in mind that it was in the context of Asian scenarios that the neutron bomb concept was first conceived. Neutron weapons would have made great sense twenty years ago, when we would first have been able to produce them. At that time the Soviets did not constitute a truly serious nuclear threat. Since then, however, the Russians have built up a huge stockpile of tactical nuclear weapons—of much better quality than ours—and they can use them against us with devastating effectiveness. This could result in our extinction.

We've got to stop pretending that we can continue being knights in shining armor and protect everybody from the Russians. It is time for us to start worrying about our own defense for a change. We must insure that we can survive the perils of the Nuclear Age. (If we really want to, we can.) But first we must stop squandering our resources on securing everyone else's survival.

We've been unbelievably derelict about preparing our own country against attack. We spend about ten times as much money trying (unsuccessfully) to protect other countries around the world than we spend protecting ourselves. Currently our strategic nuclear capabilities are weak and inadequate. This has seriously increased the possiblity of nuclear assault on America.

If our friends and allies are really serious about their own defense and survival, let them determine how to achieve it. Let them spend their own money and provide the necessary forces. If they want to, they can afford it. We cannot afford to continue trying to solve their problems. So let's not.

Instead, let's address the reality of our present inability to survive a nuclear war if it is waged against us. That's what has to come first: America. That's why I've written this book, using the neutron bomb story as an example of how a great nation, the one that brought the world into the Nuclear Age, has created a myth around these weapons and has thus pushed itself close to the brink of annihilation.

* * *

This is an ill-tempered book, not by design but rather because that's the way the words came out when I sat down to write. Usually, in my trade, which is nuclear weapons analysis, when I've finished writing a first draft of a completed study, I've had to revise and revise to make it acceptable to others in my trade—until any and all emotion or subjectivity has been removed. My opinions have had to be left out. What this means is that from a human standpoint, what I normally publish has been gutted of human value, and is of little use to the average reader.

For example, it has been fashionable for strategic thinkers and policy makers to say that there is no easy solution to the problems faced by the United States in the Nuclear Age. This may sound sagacious as all get-out, but it isn't. Actually it's trite and it's wrong. The truth—i.e., the human truth—of the matter is that if these "wise men" who decide our nation's fate were just to stop for a moment and realize that American values are not being altered by the advent of nuclear weapons, the solution would be easier to grasp. We would decide to try to survive nuclear war. We would not direct most of our concern, and most of our national defense effort, toward the preservation of others through nonnuclear war.

For some three decades I have watched our policy makers (who are mainly politicians, elected and otherwise) play at the game of nuclear policy and strategy in a world of make-believe. They have solved no problems. They have exacerbated many of them. In the context of the story of the neutron bomb, I'll describe and discuss their behavior. It will be plain that I haven't found it commendable. But I haven't been able to do a darned thing about it—except to write in anger, and hope that you'll read in anger.

This book is for people who don't claim to understand the alleged complexities of nuclear weapons issues, but who are concerned about them. I certainly haven't addressed myself to those "wise men" who constitute the national Establishment on these issues, and who claim to understand these matters. They really don't. The trouble is that Americans have felt too overwhelmed and helpless to see this and to realize the mess these guys have made. At any rate, please hear me out and decide for yourself whether to get angry or not. If you do, maybe you'll want to try to do something about it.

CHAPTER 1 INVENTING THE NEUTRON BOMB

IF I HADN'T FIGURED OUT the neutron bomb, somebody else would have. But this is true for any discovery. I just happened to figure it out before anybody else. Furthermore, I suspect it was because I am stubborn. With my determination to work things out in my own way (which means working alone), I simply had to prove my conviction that nuclear radiation was a solution to many military problems. Thirty years ago this belief made me unique. The military was convinced then that the only way to solve military problems with nuclear weapons was to blast the enemy apart. But this is jumping the gun, because before I explain how I developed the concept of the neutron bomb, I'd like to explain how I entered the field of nuclear weapons, which caused me to consider such things, and which came about totally by chance.

In 1923, when I was two years old, my father decided to move the Cohen family from Brooklyn to Los Angeles. He had visited the West Coast fifteen years earlier and had fallen in love with it, especially the climate. He was a carpenter. Los Angeles was enjoying a housing boom, and he knew he could get plenty of work. So out we went, and until 1943 I literally never left the state.

At every opportunity when I was very young, my father would take the family to the beach, or the desert or wherever else it was warm and sunny. He was a sun worshiper and turned me into one. So was my mother, who worshiped Bernarr Macfadden as well.

On May 23, 1943, while attending UCLA, I was called up by the army and shipped off to Texas for basic training, where I found that a high humidity detracted from the joys of warmth and sunbathing. In September, my basic training over, I was shipped to Cambridge, Massachusetts, to take engineering courses at the Massachusetts Institute of Technology, where the weather was delightful. It then proceeded to cool down, and by October or so, I was unhappily feeling the effects. A month later I was miserable, and one day I experienced my first snowfall. It was thrilling to see the stuff come down; it was bone-chilling to be in it.

From then on the weather turned colder and colder. I tried to stay out of it as much as possible. What I could not avoid, however, was to walk to and from classes across an open expanse between the buildings and the student cafeteria, which adjoined the student dormitory where I bunked. Two things made this walk excruciating: a strong, frigid wind that blew in from Boston Harbor, and an army regulation that prohibited earmuffs.

One day in January 1944 my concern for my delicate ears surmounted my concern about attending class and how the army might punish me if I didn't. It was about the coldest, windiest day thus far. After lunch I decided that the most comfortable distance between two points was that from the cafeteria to my bunk, where I went. Having no feelings of guilt whatsoever about missing class, and not caring about what I missed, I picked up a magazine, hopped into my bunk and happily began to read.

Suddenly the door to my room was flung open, and there stood the company sergeant. I was mortified and prepared myself for the worst. "Okay, Cohen, get off your ass, get dressed and on the double get yourself to Building X, Room Y." This I did, so relieved at not being punished for ditching classes that it never occurred to me that I was running the same frigid gauntlet that had terrified me earlier.

When I reached Room Y, a few other soldiers were waiting outside the closed door—for what, they had no more idea than I did. Finally it was my turn to go in, where two men—an army major and a middle-aged civilian—were seated. The major said practically nothing, while the civilian asked me a number of questions, mostly about my academic background, which was heavily technical. I had majored in physics at UCLA. The interview over, and no hint of what it was about, I dutifully went to class, not caring to bump into the sergeant again.

For a while I wondered about the interview. But nothing happened. I forgot about it. Two months passed, while I managed to survive the cold and began looking forward to an eastern spring, which my eastern pals told me was really something. One afternoon toward the end of March the sergeant again came to my room, and told me to be ready to ship out the next morning.

When I awoke and went off to have breakfast, an unbelievable sight awaited me: It was spring! The sky was blue, the weather was downright balmy and water was pouring off the icicles formed by a heavy snowfall a couple of days earlier. "Darnit," I told myself, "the first day of spring and I have to leave." After breakfast I went back to my room, picked up my barracks bag and went off, along with maybe twenty or twenty-five other GIs, to catch an army bus, which took us to the train station in Boston. We were told nothing as to why we were being shipped out or where we were going.

Two or three days later our train pulled into Knoxville, Tennessee, where we got off and boarded a bus that took us to some barracks on what seemed to be a military reservation under construction—yet much more than an average military reservation. We could see, as the bus drove toward the barracks, some enormous, low-slung, completely flat buildings maybe a mile or so off the road. There were no signs to tell us where we were, but as I found out later, we had come to Oak Ridge.

As I also found out much later, the MIT detachment dispatched to Oak Ridge was formed on the following basis: The major and the civilian (whose name I later learned was Tritten, and whose job was to recruit scientific personnel for the Manhattan Project, the code name for the atomic bomb project during World War II) had arrived unannounced on campus and had gone to see the president. They told him that they wished to interview as many army students as possible. However, they told the president, they did not want to interrupt classes in the process, merely wishing to interview those who were doing something else. In my case, I was goofing off, reading a magazine in my room. And that's how I got into the nuclear weapons business.

As for those who were in class that day, they stayed at MIT for a couple of months, by which time the Allied invasion of Europe had commenced and the demand for combat soldiers increased tremendously. A few of them were able to put their technical training to some use. But most of them who were fit for combat wound up as soldiers, and a good number of them were killed or wounded.

After a week or so at Oak Ridge, where I was interviewed intensively, still not having the wildest idea what was going on or what lay in store for me, I was shipped out along with twenty or thirty other soldiers. We headed west. Some days later our train pulled up at Lamy, New Mexico, a whistle-stop a few miles out of Santa Fe. Some army trucks were waiting for us, and a short time later we were in Santa Fe, in those days a beautiful small sleepy town. "Not a bad place to sit out the war," we told ourselves.

But our euphoria was short-lived. Instead of stopping, the trucks rumbled through town and out into the desert. We began getting apprehensive. For a while some joked (or half-joked) that we were going to be scientific guinea pigs for biological warfare experiments, after which we fell silent.

A half-hour later we pulled off the main highway and onto a

narrow road heading toward a series of mesas, finally winding up at Los Alamos. The Los Alamos story has been told countless times. I certainly don't want to add my version here, for two reasons: It's way off the track of what I'm writing about, and as a lowly GI doing mainly menial calculations, my knowledge of what was going on was quite limited. However, I do want to tell one story about the lab—its scientists and its director, Robert Oppenheimer—which I've never seen in print before. This anecdote concerns the moral aspects of nuclear weapons and their use, and in particular the moral issues posed by the neutron bomb.

On August 6, 1945, a terse announcement over the laboratory public-address system said that one of our "units" had been dropped over Japan and that Oppenheimer would talk about it to the scientific staff. That evening we gathered, long before the appointed time of Oppenheimer's appearance, at one of the two theaters at Los Alamos, where Oppenheimer frequently arranged for colloquia where members of the laboratory would inform the staff of progress made by their departments, or sometimes a distinguished visitor from Washington would hold forth.

Normally at one of these colloquia Oppenheimer, more or less punctual, would walk unobtrusively onstage from a wing, quiet down the audience, make a few remarks in his low-key manner and introduce the speaker. But that was not to be the case on this historic day: He was late, very late. He did not casually slip onstage from a wing. He came in from the rear of the theater, strode down the aisle and up the stairs onto the stage, and he made no effort to quiet a yelling, clapping, foot-stomping bunch of scientists who began to cheer him when he entered and continued to do so long after he got onstage.

Now, keep in mind that while this pandemonium was going on, about seventy thousand Japanese civilians lay dead in Hiroshima, with an equal number injured. About 30 percent of the victims had received lethal or injurious doses of nuclear radiation, the same kind of radiation produced by neutron weapons. Most of the scientists were, or should have been, very much aware that radiation would take a terrible toll, but at this moment of triumph they couldn't have cared less about any particular moral transgression associated with it. They were flushed with their success and they showed it. And I was one of them.

Finally Oppenheimer was able to quiet the howling crowd and he began to speak, hardly in low key. It was too early to determine what the results of the bombing might have been, but he was sure that the Japanese didn't like it. More cheering. He was proud, and he showed it, of what we had accomplished. Even more cheering. And his only regret was that we hadn't developed the bomb in time to have used it against the Germans. This practically raised the roof.

Some weeks later, the war over, Oppenheimer again addressed the staff, this time to say farewell. He was leaving to return to his academic duties. But now he was a subdued man, as were many, if not most, of the scientists. Guilt had set in. He let us know that it was our responsibility as scientists to attempt to control and even eliminate the terrible force that we had unleashed upon mankind. He had most of us in tears. Soon after that, Oppenheimer became a leader of the efforts by the United States to restrict military use of the Atom. He was appointed to a board of consultants advising the government on prospects for the international control of atomic energy. And heading the board was David Lilienthal, who later became the first chairman of the Atomic Energy Commission.

I returned to school after the war at the University of California in Berkeley, hoping to get a Ph.D. in nuclear physics. This was not to be, however. I never did like learning things for the sake of learning, and after a few months I dropped out and went back to Los Angeles, where I went to work for the RAND Corporation, the first military "think tank."

While at Los Alamos, most of my work had involved devising equations on how neutrons would behave in an atomic bomb, and then making detailed, laborious calculations by hand about how their behavior would affect the bomb's efficiency. As a matter of fact, my group was called the efficiency group, and we were charged with estimating the efficiency of the first nuclear explosion, which took place near Alamogordo, New Mexico, on July 16, 1945. (We were off by about a factor of two—on the low side. We predicted eleven kilotons; it went off at almost twenty kilotons.) Later, at Berkeley, I worked part time at the university's famous radiation laboratory, at that time probably the world's foremost center of nuclear radiation research. So by the time I arrived at RAND, I had a smattering of knowledge about nuclear radiation.

Shortly after coming to RAND, I was assigned the job of making calculations pertaining to radiological warfare, i.e., the military use of nuclear radiation emitted by certain radioactive materials. This involved schemes where these radioactive materials would be dispersed over an area to irradiate enemy troops with gamma rays (which are like very high-energy X rays). Hopefully this would kill them or at least make their traversal through, or occupation of, the area very hazardous. Thus, my entry into the world of hostile nuclear radiation commenced, a world I've remained in up to now.

Speaking candidly and truthfully, I will say that I've never had any moral qualms or feelings of guilt about my pursuits in this military field. I have always believed that the United States must have strong and effective military forces—especially nuclear forces. I have always considered my type of work essential for the nation's security. And as for my investigations into the military uses of radiation, frankly I have found them challenging and fascinating. Why I've been drawn—very much alone, I might say—to a subject that has instilled both fear and moral repugnance in the minds of most people, I don't know. I've plumbed my psyche, which I'm sure many would regard as perverse, searching the reasons why, to no avail.

When I left Los Alamos, along with practically everybody else I took a souvenir of this unforgettable experience. In my case, since a friend was a metallurgist who had helped fabricate the uranium components for the bomb that destroyed Hiroshima, the souvenir was a small cylinder, about the size of one's pinkie, of natural uranium. It was worth maybe a dime or a quarter. Upon joining RAND, to impress people I placed the cylinder of uranium on my desk.

One day a consultant who was assisting me with my radiological warfare calculations dropped in to chat. He noticed the cylinder, picked it up, juggled it in his hands for a while and exclaimed, "This is pretty dense stuff, isn't it? What is it?"

I decided to play games with him and said, "Why don't you guess, Milt."

Of course, his first guess was lead.

"Nope," I said, "try again."

He thought for a little bit and tried tungsten.

"Nope, try once more," I said.

Finally he ran out of guesses and said "Okay, I give up. Tell me."

I told him what it was. He blanched, put it down, and a minute or two later (the time he figured it would take to salvage his endangered machismo), he excused himself to go to the men's room. When he came back, his hands had been scrubbed red.

Milt's professional credentials in the area of nuclear physics and radiation were impeccable. He had been one of the select few working with the great scientist Niels Bohr in Copenhagen before the war, where nuclear fission of uranium had been discovered. He had written one of the early papers on the subject. From a technical standpoint he had an exquisite understanding of what was happening in the piece of metal in his hands and the possible radiation danger it posed. He knew there was no conceivable danger. He knew that he could have taped the uranium to his groin and left it there for the rest of his life with no threat to his potency, his fertility, or to his genes and chromosomes. Yet he was frightened over the possible consequences of being "contaminated" by the radiation.

Even stranger was the fact that, unlike any average person who might have behaved as Milt did, he was reacting psychologically to something that, intellectually, he fully understood. He knew all about what he couldn't see or feel. He would have scoffed at anyone who professed to fear radiation because it was invisible, and would have accused such a person of mythology and superstition. Yet he was unable to avoid showing his own mythological fear—a fear held by many respected scientists who know better intellectually but are emotionally helpless to look objectively at issues involving the military use of nuclear radiation.

In the spring of 1948 the Defense Department and the Atomic Energy Commission appointed a committee to investigate the potential for radiological warfare. My boss was named to the committee to provide estimates of the radiation effects for various radiological weapon concepts. He was a rather lazy person, so he pulled me into the act to do his work for him.

The committee's charter was to examine the vista of military applications for selective radioactive materials. This would cover such possibilities as attacking enemy troop positions, putting up a zone of radioactive contamination to kill or incapacitate advancing enemy soldiers, heavily contaminating key transportation junctions to deny passage by enemy vehicles, and so on.

In those days, to produce the required radioactive agent it was necessary to use our relatively primitive nuclear reactors. (The reactors would produce neutrons that in turn would be absorbed in the material to be made radioactive, a process known in the trade as "neutron-induced radioactivity." Representative of such materials are compounds containing sodium or tantalum.) The reactor technology at that time represented an extremely inefficient production scheme. Then there was the problem of shipping the material to the combat theater, which meant that considerable decay would occur before it was applied. Moreover, there was the problem of the heavy radiation shielding needed to allow safe handling, transport and military delivery, which at that time could be effected only by manned aircraft. After considering and analyzing all these problems, the committee found it difficult to wax optimistic about the near-term future of radiological warfare.

For some months the committee toiled in this nuclear vineyard, reached its findings and put its summary report together. It was then arranged for us to present our results to a number of high-ranking Washington officials and distinguished scientists consulting with the government. On a Sunday morning (the only time possible to get all the invited officials to attend, at the risk of further increasing the unhappiness of their poor families, who saw precious little of Papa during the working week, which included Saturdays) our presentation took place. But hardly as expected.

Naturally, when the appointed time came, few of the dignitaries had arrived. This, of course, was standard behavior for the high and mighty; a brand of gamesmanship always practiced by those in lofty official positions. The more luminous the dignitary, the more he feels it necessary to avoid showing up ahead of the lesser lights, of whom I was the least. Finally all but one of the dignitaries had arrived. This was David Lilienthal, chairman of the Atomic Energy Commission and the most prestigious member of the meeting.

When Lilienthal ultimately did show up, very late indeed, he walked in and went to the head of the conference table to a place bearing his name. But he did not sit down and wait for the meeting to get started. Instead, he stood at his place and began a very brief impromptu speech. He told us that he had come essentially against his will but, for reasons of protocol, felt that he had to put in an appearance. He found the subject at hand to be extremely distasteful; he was appalled that such activities were going on; his view, as chairman of the AEC, was that he preferred to preside over the control and peaceful applications of the Atom, and he certainly had no desire to attend meetings such as this one. Then, having gotten his feelings off his chest, he left the room. We were shattered.

The meeting itself, after Lilienthal's performance, was effectively over. We presented our findings to a group that now, because of Lilienthal's remarks, was inclined to be unreceptive. And since our findings did not contain a glowing account of prospects for radiological warfare, it was easy for the officials to yield to their inclinations to ignore the issue. So this was essentially the end of the line for radiological warfare. Everything would be done with atomic bombs. This has been the case ever since.

Although I had no quarrel with the committee's findings, I did feel there was something to the matter of radiological warfare. More accurately, I felt there was a potential use for nuclear radiation in this particular fashion. Our findings had been based on the technology at hand. Nobody had attempted to plumb future technological possibilities, involving different nuclear technologies, to see if the future might hold greater promise. The idea of someday having neutron warheads of very low explosive power, which could be used to produce radioactive agents, was never entertained by anyone. Had anyone proposed this possibility, he would have been laughed out of the room.

With the first procreational effort for the military use of nuclear radiation resulting in a stillbirth, I applied myself to more mundane (if you will pardon the use of that word) applications of atomic bombs. In those days such uses were all strategic, meaning the bombing of cities. I became, in the parlance of those who hold population bombing to be morally wrong, a "baby killer." At the same time though, I always had radiation in the back of my mind. Which brings to mind a colossal intellectual disaster that I suffered at my own hands.

In January 1950 President Truman made the decision to proceed with the development of the hydrogen bomb. His decision came after a particularly intense and bitter national debate, during which the opposition, spearheaded by Oppenheimer, had argued among other reasons that more effective military capabilities could be achieved by improving atomic bomb technology. Later on that year the air force asked RAND to study this issue. I became a member of the study group, and one of my chores was to estimate the extent of the radiation effects of hydrogen bombs. I picked up my slide rule* and began to calculate. The results were amazing, unbelievably so.

It turned out that contrary to practically everyone's expectations, the hydrogen bomb would be a radiation bomb. Its gamma rays, which would be created by the absorption of neutrons in the atmosphere, would extend well beyond the effects of blast and heat. This was not supposed to be. It was against sound physical intuition. But then, numbers don't lie.

I checked and double-checked the calculations, and they came out the same. My boss, who was torn between suspicion and a desire to put his department (and himself) on the map by revealing these results, had me check them with other scientists at RAND. They checked out. The air force was informally told about it. I became a bit of a celebrity. Strangely enough, however, even though this had to be somewhat earthshaking, no other scientists seemed shaken enough to want to do their own calculations to determine the accuracy of mine. But by now I had begun to become more and more suspicious that it was too good to be true, and every so often, this business preying on my mind, I would put my feet up on my desk and mentally go through the calculations. They always checked out.

One day the smartest man in the world came to consult with RAND. This was John von Neumann, a mathematician and scientist; a genius of the highest order who at that time was with

* My dad gave me this slide rule on my fifteenth birthday. I used it to make the first neutron bomb radiation-effects calculations. I still use it. I can't even operate a pocket calculator.

Einstein and other geniuses at Princeton's Institute for Advanced Study. Probably the best reason why he deserved to be called the smartest man in the world was because all the self-styled smartest men in the world who met him agreed that he was smarter than they were. Let me give you an example of how smart that guy was.

While I was at Los Alamos, where von Neumann consulted on occasion, my friend in the office across the hall, Wayne, worked out an equation. Whereas he was bright enough to develop the equation, he was unable to solve it. After a few days of trying, he gave up and passed it on to others. They tried and gave up. They were very smart guys, too. It was decided that the equation would have to be solved with the help of calculating machines when machine time became available. In the meantime Wayne chalked the equation in the corner of his blackboard, with a sign underneath offering a reward to anyone who solved it.

One day von Neumann showed up at the lab. Unless he had something specific to do, his habits were mainly peripatetic: walking up and down halls, poking his head into offices, and if something looked interesting, he would stop and chat. On this day he hall-walked.

When he came to Wayne's office, he looked in and saw the equation and the reward sign. He stopped, stared into space for a few minutes, walked up to the blackboard and wrote out the solution. Then he left, without bothering to claim the reward, and with Wayne so transfixed by this performance that he couldn't even get up to chase von Neumann down the hall to give it to him.

Getting back to von Neumann's visit to RAND, it was decided that he ought to go over my H-bomb calculations with me. So I explained the whole thing to him, point by point, number by number. He agreed that I was correct and that was that; I had the concurrence of the brightest of the bright.

This should have put my uneasiness to rest. But it didn't. I continued my mental checking, until one day—*it didn't check.* I was half mortified and half relieved. I checked my noncheck and the noncheck held up. It showed that my original calculation was off by a factor of almost, get this: *one thousand.* There's no point here in trying to explain the original mistake I made, and remade, and which nobody caught, except to say that I had made a cardinal error that no self-respecting scientist should make—I had gone against physical intuition. At that time the effects of nuclear weapons were pretty well understood. One hardly had to go through detailed calculations to prove that the bigger the bang, the smaller the radiation effects become (relative to those of blast and heat). This had been proven at Hiroshima and Nagasaki, and those two A-bombs were only one-thousandth or so the bang of a respectable H-bomb. So how in heaven's name could these respectable scientists (of which I was not one, but at least I caught the error) have gotten so far off-base?

I got up, walked into my boss's office and told him where I had gone wrong. He knew it was true, but his problem was in explaining this to the air force. This he did, after desperately searching for some technical factor I might have omitted. And nothing happened. The air force, which always had been concerned mainly with blasting and burning down cities, couldn't have cared less.

Suppose the scientific data I used for my calculations had been different, that I had not made the stupid mistake I did and that the results had come out the same: namely, that the radiation effects would extend well beyond the effects of blast and heat. The hydrogen bomb would have been a giant version of the neutron bomb. (H-bombs are based on the same kinds of nuclear reactions as neutron bombs: i.e., fusion reactions, involving the heavy nuclei of hydrogen—deuterium and tritium.) Well, I would have discovered the principle of the neutron bomb years before I actually did. In fact, I would have discovered a superneutron bomb, since at that time H-bombs had an explosive power about one thousand times as great as N-bombs. A few handfuls of these super N-bombs could have wiped out the entire Red Army if it were trying to invade Europe, without destroying Europe.

Had I actually produced an honest to gosh super N-bomb concept in 1950, would it have changed the scheme of things? I doubt it. My guess is that the air force would have told the Atomic Energy Commission to get cracking on an H-bomb design that didn't waste all that energy on radiation, and develop one that maximized blast and heat—especially blast. (I recall one visit I made around this time to the headquarters of the Strategic Air Command, where I spoke with its commander, General Curtis E. LeMay. When we got around to discussing SAC's requirements for advanced hydrogen bombs, LeMay told me that his ultimate requirement was for "you guys to develop a bomb that could destroy all of Russia.")

I got hooked on tactical nuclear weapons (neutron bombs falling into this category) in 1951, which was a turning point in my life. A friend of mine, who worked for the air force in the Pentagon, asked if I would be interested in going to Korea for a few weeks on a "secret" mission, to see if, in my opinion, there was any good way to use atomic bombs in that war. The purpose of my visit over there was to be carefully guarded, because at that time the air force, which was almost totally SAC-dominated (SAC, in those days, spelled *LeMay*), was locked in a bitter battle with the U.S. scientific community (which, in those days, spelled *Oppenheimer*) over the issue of tactical nuclear weapons.

LeMay was dead set against *any* tactical nuclear capability, by *any* U.S. military service. He regarded efforts in this direction as a direct threat to SAC's strategic H-bomb capability, which he was convinced would solve any and all military problems. Oppenheimer, meanwhile, had begun a campaign to promote the use of tactical nuclear weapons in Europe, where the NATO military buildup had just gotten underway. He had expressed his views on these weapons early that year:

> ... one thing is very clear. It is clear that they [nuclear weapons] can be used only as adjuncts in a military campaign which has some other components, and whose purpose is a military victory. They are not primarily weapons of totality or terror, but weapons used to give combat forces help that they would otherwise lack. They are an integral part of military operations. Only when the atomic bomb is recognized as useful insofar as it is an integral part of military operations, will it really be of much help in the fighting of a war, rather than in warning all mankind to avert it.*

My Pentagon friend, a pretty courageous guy, obviously did not want to get himself mixed up in this imbroglio. And so our agree-

* From a speech, "Comments on the Military Value of the Atom," given to the American Bar Association in February 1951.

ment was that my Korean trip was to be an "orientation tour," to acquaint me with the nature of war by actually observing a war being fought. While I was there, I was to keep to myself any ideas I picked up about how atomic weapons might be used, for fear that somebody might get the idea that we were seriously contemplating such use. After I returned home, I could discuss my ideas freely.

Off I went to Korea, for my first trip outside the U.S. I was put on a troop-transport aircraft, jammed with infantrymen and their weapons, and after forever and a day, or so it seemed droning along at 150 mph, I finally arrived at an air base outside Seoul. From there I hopped a jeep ride to the headquarters of the United Nations command, which was to be my base of operation.

The first thought that struck me about the use of nuclear weapons occurred when I was crossing a bridge over the Han River to go into Seoul. The bridge, of very sturdy construction, looked like a lunar landscape. It was pockmarked all over with craters from just about every kind of bomb we had used to try to destroy it and stop the North Korean soldiers before they could get into Seoul. Once they entered the city, it would be a terrible fight to push them out. Street-by-street combat is no picnic for those trying to evict the defenders, and it usually devastates the city. This is exactly what happened to Seoul because, after hundreds and hundreds of bombing sorties, we couldn't knock down the bridge over the Han. It was just too tough.

As we drove across the bridge, I thought, "What an ideal spot for an atomic bomb." This thought surely had to have occurred to many others, particularly the pilots who saw their bombs actually explode on the bridge with no results. What did not cross my mind at that time was what the consequences would have been to the city of Seoul if we had blown up the bridge with a nuclear weapon representative of that period, namely, an atomic bomb of the type we used to destroy Nagasaki. At any rate, Seoul was a mess, the likes of which I had never imagined, despite seeing all the war pictures earlier. Take a look at the two photos of Hiroshima and Seoul and ask yourself which city suffered the most damage. You probably can't see any difference, which brings up the dilemma of whether to use nuclear weapons against such tactical targets as key bridges in the Korean War—namely, you are damned if you do and damned if you don't.

U.S. Army Photograph #SC 290666.

Hiroshima, Japan, October 12, 1945.

U.S. Army Photograph #SC 352260.

Seoul, Korea, November 1, 1950.

Had we knocked out the bridge on the River Han with a Nagasaki-sized bomb and destroyed Seoul in the process, there would have been hell to pay. The guilt syndrome produced by the nuclear bombings of Japan prevailed over much of the Western world. America would have been roundly condemned by most countries, including our UN allies—except the South Koreans, who might gladly have suffered the loss of Seoul (which they did anyway) if nuking the bridge had ended the hostilities. As it was, not destroying the bridge led to a vicious struggle to kick the Communists out of Seoul. It also involved heavy American casualties and did not end the war.

Had neutron weapons been available to help drive out the North Koreans, the city of Seoul would have looked about the same after the bombing as before. I'm not implying here that seeing Seoul in ruins put the neutron bomb bee in my bonnet, but it certainly did make me wonder about the advisability of using atomic bombs of the 1950's vintage to force the enemy out of cities.

Upon returning from Korea, I reported to the air force on my ideas for using tactical nuclear weapons in the Korean conflict. I had concluded that there was an extensive target system for such use. However, there was no receptivity for my notions. The air force remained adamantly against using nuclear weapons for tactical warfare. They continued to regard atomic bombs as weapons of "totality" and "terror." They wanted H-bombs capable of blowing the Russians off the map and out of the war.

At this time I was requested to present my views to a couple of Oppenheimer's scientific colleagues from Cal Tech, who had worked closely with him in his efforts to promote tactical nuclear weapons. I thought they would be receptive. They weren't. In fact, they were aghast that anyone would consider using atomic weapons again in Asia. The only theater for nuclear use they could think of was Europe. This was my first exposure to the "Hiroshima syndrome," and the intensity of the belief that we should never use atomic weapons against Asians again. This conviction still reigns in many quarters of the U.S. government, and it has been instrumental in shaping our tactical nuclear weapons policy. This applies to our current policy on the neutron bomb as well.

* * *

I went to Europe the next year to brief U.S. military personnel on a tactical nuclear study I had completed and to get acquainted with NATO's efforts in this area. It was 1952, and much of the destruction from World War II was still evident. Once again I was impressed and affected by the extent of the urban damage resulting from conventional war.

When I arrived in Germany, NATO had just initiated its first study on the requirements for employing tactical nuclear weapons. I was invited to participate in the program, which was under the direction of an air force officer, Colonel Hal Watson, and was dominated by air force thinking. In no time at all I had made myself persona non grata, when I pointed out that it was obvious that the biggest bombs were being favored for use against targets that were located mainly around cities. Meanwhile, the battlefield, which after all, was where the main tactics of the war would be employed—was being short-shrifted.

"Holy cow, Colonel," I would argue, "if you put this bomb on this bridge or railroad yard in Zilchburg, there goes Zilchburg." My concern over Zilchburg only succeeded in antagonizing the colonel, who saw no reason to worry about the city in setting about to demolish the target. For reasons like this, NATO started off by establishing its preference for big atomic bombs and has, to a very large degree, retained such weapons. However, not only did this not concern the colonel with whom I argued, but it seemed not to worry anyone else in the American military. This included the officer in charge of the whole NATO shooting match, General Alfred Grunther, who told the National Security Industrial Association, in an address on September 29, 1954: ". . . simply because atomic bombs do create casualties—and very heavy casualties against women and children—there is no reason why we should become sentimental over this question as to what weapons must be used. The chore is to make war itself impossible."

Upon returning from Europe I spent a couple of years trying to understand the tactical nuclear business. I established a good working relationship with the newly created nuclear weapons laboratory at Livermore, California. During this period I first began to apply myself to the question of what the tactical uses for nuclear weapons might be, especially on the battlefield. It was in the course of these investigations that I became convinced that nuclear radiation was the way to go. My views had considerable effect on the Livermore program, but just about none back in the Pentagon. The military was darkly suspicious of radiation. They preferred to do all jobs by blasting the targets apart. Standard military procedure had been to assess target damage by looking at photographs of the results of an attack on the enemy in deciding what to do next. If the enemy target looked about the same after an attack as before (as it would if radiation were used), it could really be confusing for the military mind.

I shifted over to the strategic nuclear area in the mid-1950's, mainly on the defensive side. I was creating new concepts for using nuclear bursts to defend against bomber and ballistic missile attacks on the United States. Naturally I concentrated on schemes involving radiation.

In those days bombers were being designed to fly as high and fast as possible, to make the job of defending interceptors as tough as possible. However, from the standpoint of using nuclear radiation, neutrons in particular, the higher the bomber would fly, the more rarefied the atmosphere, and the further out the neutrons would go. I made some rough calculations on how far the neutron effects from a large thermonuclear warhead, delivered by rocket, would reach to incapacitate the crews of high-flying bombers. The results were impressive. The neutron effects considerably exceeded the effects of blast and heat that would be required to destroy the bombers.

"Why don't you calculate the neutron effects from bursting your warhead real high, out of the atmosphere?" suggested my colleague Henry Alden, a descendant of John. I did this. Now the results were really impressive, with the neutrons beaming down on the poor Russian bomber crews like a giant sunlamp. So we called the concept Henry's Sunlamp. I went back to SAC headquarters to brief LeMay and company on Sunlamp, and in turn, what the implications of a Soviet Sunlamp capability might be for SAC. LeMay, who had always maintained that his bombers could outfox the defenses, was shaken a little. When I finished my briefing, he sat quietly for a while, then rose, turned around and told his commanders: "We'll find a way to deal with this threat."

They never did. On the other hand, the Russian Sunlamp threat never materialized.

The air force showed only a momentary interest in this defensive concept, because around that time it began to look like the Russians were concentrating on intercontinental ballistic missiles (ICBMs). The interest in defending against bombers disappeared. So I decided to see how effective the neutrons might be against an ICBM attack.

I was pleasantly surprised for my calculations showed that neutrons would cause the high explosive in the nuclear warhead of an ICBM to decompose to such a degree that the warhead probably wouldn't function. I was asked to present my findings to Bennie Schriever, the air force general in charge of our ICBM program, which had then just barely gotten underway. Bennie decided to bring in one of his consultants to check out my calculations. Guess who the consultant was? Why, von Neumann, of course.

This time my calculations were pretty good, and von Neumann, who was pretty careful in checking them, concurred. The so-called "neutron kill" received serious attention. Somewhat later we realized that the fissionable material in the warhead was even more susceptible than the high explosive, and many years later a neutron warhead of the same general type we're now producing for tactical use was developed for the Sprint anti-ICBM defensive missile.

In the summer of 1958 the air force convened a group of scientists in Puerto Rico to explore the technical vista for enhancing limited-war capabilities. Because of the Korean War and the French experience in Indochina, such wars were in vogue in those days and were expected to continue into the future. However, in the event of a Soviet attack on NATO, there would probably be all-out nuclear war. It was expected that *that* war would be won by SAC bombing the living daylights out of Russia. With the promise of such a "massive retaliation" against the USSR should it attack Europe, it was believed that this war would never start. And since the limited wars to date had been fought in Asia, it was expected that they would continue to be fought in Asia: another war in Korea; another war in Indochina; a Chinese invasion of Taiwan or Thailand; the Soviets invading Iran, and so on.

Joining this group was my old boss, the guy who, because he was lazy, had gotten me onto the radiological warfare committee in 1948. His task on this effort was to hold down the tactical nuclear weapons slot. This was a thankless assignment if there ever was one, since there was little chance that the air force, still dominated by SAC, would show any interest in this area. History repeated itself, and sure enough, I got a call from him asking me to come aboard, which meant that he would pontificate and I would do the work. But I'd never been to Puerto Rico and it seemed like too nice a trip to pass up. So I obliged.

Since it had been a few years since I had visited Livermore to find out what new research was going on, when we left Puerto Rico to pursue our assignments, I called my friend Johnny Foster, who was in charge of work related to low-yield nuclear explosives, and told him that I'd like to go over his program. "Sure," he said, "come on up."

When I arrived, Johnny reviewed the parts of his section's work that seemed related to my task. There was nothing really new since what I'd heard during my last visit. Then he suggested that I might be interested in hearing about a couple of ideas that seemed to have nothing directly to do with tactical nuclear weapons, but which he thought held some intriguingly new technology: specifically, fusion technology.

The first idea was to utilize a minimal amount of fission-produced energy to trigger fusion reactions. This type of reaction involves the heavy nuclei of hydrogen, which produce the neutron bomb's neutrons. Most of the yield of this device would come from these fusion reactions, which do not release dangerous radioactivity. The second idea was for what we call a pure-fusion device. It would use no fissile material whatsoever, requiring instead an ingenious detonating mechanism to trigger the fusion reactions.

The potential applications of these ideas were mainly for nonmilitary purposes, where nuclear explosives could be used for commercial blasting purposes—digging canals, loosening ore deposits, releasing underground caches of natural gas, etc.—without producing vast amounts of long-lived, dangerous radioactivity. In fact, one of these ideas had been code-named Dove, which clearly implied a peaceful application.

Both these ideas represented very low explosive-power versions of the thermonuclear warheads I had considered when making calculations for bomber and ICBM defense. Like my high-yield warheads, they were prodigious producers of neutrons. Naturally, sensing that they might be especially effective weapons for battlefield application by using the radiation against enemy personnel, I asked how good they might be as neutron emitters. The answer was "pretty damned good," and they provided me with some off-the-cuff estimates of what types of neutrons might escape from these devices, and how many.

Upon returning to my office, I took out the slide rule my dad had given me, picked up a handbook containing data on blast and heat effects, and proceeded to make some calculations on the nature of these nuclear explosives. And being battle-scarred from the previous H-bomb experience, I made doubly sure not to make any stupid mistakes. Fifteen or twenty minutes later the neutron bomb concept emerged. What appeared realistically at hand was a battlefield weapon that could be used like the legendary Death Ray. By bursting the fusion device high off the ground, only the enemy-killing radiation would reach the ground; the blast and heat intensities that might reach the ground would not be powerful enough to cause any significant damage to built-up areas. This concept was in sharp contrast to that behind the battlefield fission weapons that we had deployed overseas at the time (and which are still deployed). Their use made large-scale physical damage unavoidable. There was another important difference—in the production of long-lived radioactivity. The fission-fusion neutron weapon would produce only one one-hundredth or even less of the radioactivity produced by a fission weapon with the same battlefield effectiveness, i.e., the same enemy troop killing power. The pure-fusion neutron weapon would produce none of the dangerous, long-term radioactivity produced by fission weapons.

While I didn't exactly burst out with a "Eureka," I was quite excited. For this was, really and truly, the first battlefield-weapon concept in history which would allow a guaranteed, highly effective defense against an invading enemy without producing wholesale physical destruction of the country being invaded. At the same time though, I felt a bit insecure about my findings. They were based on relatively simple calculations, and as any expert knows, the mechanics of neutrons bouncing around in the atmosphere are extremely complex. Not being able to understand and analyze such complex physical problems, I decided to check with an expert who could. This was my pal Jess, and I want to talk about him, to give you an idea of how many a brilliant scientist can become motivated because of a consuming passion for a subject totally unrelated to his scientific pursuits.

Jess was born and raised in Knoxville, where his father was a professor at the University of Tennessee. He was brought up to be a law-abiding citizen with a moral code that frowned on certain obvious iniquities, such as gambling. He became interested in science and engineering, and after graduating from college, he worked, during World War II, on the development of radar. After the war he gravitated to RAND, where he worked on the theory of radar detection, which called for an understanding of mathematical statistics.

At the beginning of this work Jess knew just about nothing about statistics. He had never taken courses on the subject in college. So he had to educate himself, which he did in short order, mastering the subject in the process. Using his newly acquired mathematical prowess, he quickly became one of the real experts on radar detection and contributed significantly to the development of SAC's radar bombing equipment.

One summer day in 1950, when we were returning to work after lunch, I decided that instead of going back to my desk, I'd go to Hollywood Park racetrack, which was just a fifteen- or twenty-minute drive from RAND. "Come along," I said to Jess. I had asked him many times before and he always had refused, not because of guilt over skipping work but because of his qualms about gambling.

"Look," I said, "there's no law which says you have to bet at the track. Let me do the betting and you can watch the horses run. It's pretty exciting." His resistance collapsed and off we went.

The day turned out to be a lucky one for me, and after three or four races I was a few bucks ahead. What was going on in Jess's mind, watching the horses and watching me win, I'll never know, but with the next race coming up, suddenly his moral reservations collapsed and he bet two dollars to show on the favorite. The favorite won, and Jess contemplated his first winning bet. Of course, he bet on the following race, and won again. When the last race was over, he had bet to place and even to win, and was comfortably ahead for his efforts. He was also hooked on horse racing and betting.

We began going to the track together on a fairly frequent basis. Jess even began to go by himself. He became absorbed with the art of odds-making and decided to turn it into a science. This involved getting hundreds of back copies of the *Daily Racing Form,* studying all the factors that determine a horse's performance (weight impost, track condition, jockey's record, etc.), and then doing an analysis, based on Jess's grasp of mathematical statistics, to figure out what the odds should be in the horse's next race. This enabled him to compare his estimated odds with those established by the bettors at the track just before the race was run. If the bettors had sufficiently overestimated the odds on some horse (for example, they were sending the horse to the post at ten-to-one odds when Jess thought that five-to-one was more realistic) Jess would bet on the horse. In track parlance, this would be betting an "overlay."

His system worked so well at the track, which was taking a 10 percent cut of the money bet in those days, that he decided to test his skill against that of the Las Vegas bookies, who took no cut at all. On weekends he would grab a plane to Vegas, head for the bookie joints and bet. He began to win. Soon he came to the conclusion that he could make more money, in a more interesting way, betting on the horses at Vegas than calculating radars at RAND. So he took a leave of absence from scholarly propriety and began a new life. He made out like a bandit.

A year or so later Jess became the first guy in Las Vegas history to be barred from betting at the bookie joints. He was unbeatable, and they saw no point in contributing unduly to his bankroll. With that, he returned, somewhat unhappily, to a life of moral rectitude at RAND. However, by now calculating odds was in his blood. Little by little he began to play at other games, while analyzing them mathematically to find out where he stood best to profit, substantially improving his statistical abilities in the process.

He began applying his mathematical prowess to blackjack and poker, and became a top-notch player of both. These nefarious pursuits also provided him with powerful mathematical tools for calculating nuclear radiation effects. In 1956 he became absorbed in this subject, and shortly thereafter emerged as perhaps the foremost expert in the country on the transmission of neutrons and gamma rays in various media.

On the sinful side of his life Jess moved into the select circle of Las Vegas gamblers and could hold his own against the best of them. He became interested in odds-making for various sports, where he acquired the respect—even adulation—of such legendary figures as Jimmy the Greek, who on one occasion called Jess for advice on establishing impeachment odds for Richard Nixon. Jess told him to put up odds of one-thousand-to-one against impeachment, not because he had calculated the mood of the Senate, but because he figured that Nixon was nobody's fool and would resign as soon as he saw that he might be impeached.

Anyway, Jess was always willing to help a friend and was generous with his time, so he immediately took time off from his assigned duties and set up a mathematical model for calculating the neutron effects from these "peaceful" explosives. It turned out that I had been pretty lucky with my "back-of-the-envelope" calculations. His results approximated mine. The neutron bomb had been anointed by scientific respectability.

All this had come about because of my air force assignment, so to fulfill this commitment I dutifully wrote a report describing the concept in the context of limited-war application. (The report was innocuously titled "Limited Nuclear Weapons in Limited Nuclear War.") I also prepared a briefing and waited for a request to deliver it to an air force audience in the Pentagon. The invitation came a couple of months later. During the years that followed my first neutron bomb briefing, I gave the pitch dozens and dozens of times. I gave most of them in the Washington area (where politicians, in civvies or in military uniform, elected or appointed, fought over my pink body), and in military commands ranging from Pearl Harbor to Naples, where service politics dictated interest or disinterest. I'll give you a sample briefing later on.

CHAPTER 2 PEDDLING THE NEUTRON BOMB

IN ONE OF THE OLD Marx brothers' movies, there is a scene in which Groucho and his inamorata, Margaret Dumont, are locked in a mad embrace on the sofa. There is a knock on the door. "Who is it?" says Groucho, plainly annoyed with the interruption. "The garbage man," says the voice on the outside. "We don't want any," replies Groucho.

If we were to look back over the history of the neutron bomb and scrutinize and analyze the attitude of the U.S. government toward it, we'd find that, on balance, the response to the concept of this weapon has been "we don't want any." Even when the United States finally made neutron warheads, the government was badly split over the decision. The potential recipients of these weapons, our NATO allies, wanted no part of them.

As pointed out previously, the air force's attitude toward tactical nuclear weapons, especially those for battlefield use, had not changed. One could have predicted what the response would be when I appeared before my first air force audience, a very small audience indeed, to give my briefing: "We don't want any."

On the other hand, there were a few civilians in the audience who weren't beholden (out of fear) to the military party line. They seemed intrigued with the concept. They asked me to hang around to give a second briefing to a more diverse group, including some of their cronies in the army and navy. During that briefing, an old navy acquaintance of mine, Admiral Chick Hayward, who had gotten in on the ground floor of the nuclear weapons business right after the war, showed up and I could see a spark of interest. But there was no positive reaction from the army.

That second briefing appeared to be the last I would give. Weeks went by and there was no request for a repeat performance. "Well, there goes another idea down the drain," I told myself. So I went about earning my daily bread at RAND.

Then, just before Christmas, when I was visiting back in Washington, a colleague called me and asked if I had the time to get together with a friend of his to explain the concept. His friend was a navy officer who was a special assistant to the chairman of the AEC for national security matters: Captain Morse. Before joining the AEC, Jack Morse had been in charge of nuclear weapons planning at SHAPE (Supreme Headquarters Allied Powers in Europe, NATO's military command, organized by Dwight Eisenhower in 1951). During his tour at SHAPE he had picked up strong convictions that NATO must acquire a highly discriminate tactical nuclear stockpile if it were to have a credible capability for defending Western Europe.

Of course I had the time. Poor Jack, who was on the ragged edge of being legally blind and was about to enter the hospital for a cataract operation, got no more than a couple of feet from my briefing charts, occasionally reducing the distance to inches to be able to read the finer print. Unlike my air force audience, he bombarded me with questions. When I was through, he explained to me that he would be out of things for a while because of his operation, but that I would be hearing from him. My concept was precisely what he had been looking for. He wanted to parade me around certain Washington quarters as soon as he got out of the hospital.

No sooner had his bandages been removed, than Jack picked up the phone by his bed and began to make calls. Understandably he called the navy. He arranged to have me brief a freshly promoted rear admiral, Tom Moorer, who had been put in charge of the navy's long-range objectives section in the Pentagon. (A dozen years later Moorer had climbed to the top of the military ladder, becoming Chairman of the Joint Chiefs of Staff.) I was about to be adopted.

Let's pause for a moment and take stock of the Washington milieu in which I was about to become immersed while peddling my neutron bomb.

The date was early 1959. In the Pentagon the air force remained supreme in nuclear weapons capabilities, even in tactical nuclear capabilities, albeit of the wrong kind (very highly destructive). The army, which was amassing a stockpile of battlefield nuclear weapons, had little affection for these weapons because they could not figure out how to use them without a massive overhauling of traditional doctrine and force structure, which is something that no venerable military organization wants to do. Meanwhile, the navy was desperately searching for ways and means to justify its role of providing aircraft carriers. It was being forced out of strategic bombing by SAC. And with the possibility of large-scale conventional wars essentially excluded by the Eisenhower military policy, there was no way to advance its cause in this arena. However, in the limited-war arena, where its highly mobile, extended-range carrier forces could register a peacetime presence in potential hot spots, the navy was ready to jump at the first opportunity to show that carrier-based aircraft could, almost immediately, provide a credible and effective tactical nuclear capability. Or so it seemed.

In the Pentagon, in the Atomic Energy Commission and in certain powerful quarters of the Congress, there was an uneasiness over the moratorium on nuclear testing that the United States and the USSR had unofficially agreed to in the fall of 1958. There were some who thought the Soviets would cheat during this moratorium. Most likely they were right. There were others who held that the Soviet ploy, by seeming to observe the moratorium, was to have the U.S. allow its capabilities to deteriorate while they (the Soviets) prepared for a new series of tests. This group turned out to be dead right. Meanwhile, many of them were looking for ways to pressure Eisenhower and force him to resume testing.

The nuclear climate was different in the White House, however. The President, despite previous avowals to the contrary, had opted for nuclear arms control and had initiated talks with the Russians with the intention of putting an end to nuclear testing. (The talks still go on, and on.) The worldwide fears over the radioactive fallout from hydrogen bomb testing during the early and mid-1950s had pushed him, not only into these talks but also into a pledge to suspend all nuclear testing for an unspecified period, so long as the Russians did the same. Whether he knew it or not, Ike had entered into an unverifiable test-ban agreement. There was no way to detect low-yield underground tests the Soviets might conduct clandestinely (which they almost undoubtedly did), and which could quite possibly have included neutron bomb tests. Also, whether he knew it or not, Ike had effectively established himself as an opponent of the testing of low-yield tactical nuclear weapons, including neutron bombs. Lastly, whether he knew it or not, he had come under the influence of a group of White House scientific advisors who had dedicated themselves to nuclear arms control. (They were going to assume tremendous political power when their favorite presidential candidate, John F. Kennedy, came into office.)

In essence, the Washington military-political scene could be described as a White House island of resistance to the neutron bomb concept located in a sea of government agencies and institutions that mainly seemed to favor the concept. As seen through the eyes of those who have always been suspicious of nuclear test bans (I'm one of them), those were the good old days, when independent points of view in the government about newfangled ideas could be registered and advanced. But those days are long gone. Today our test-ban position rests on the alleged need to make only the most pedestrian of changes in our nuclear stockpile and ascertain that those weapons in the stockpile will actually work.

It was in this political climate that I began my sales campaign. And I was as innocent of these politics as a newborn babe. When I got a favorable reaction from someone whom I had briefed, my ego took over and I decided that not only had I done a good job of pushing the product, but that the Bomb itself was being accepted for what it was worth. Better yet, for what *I* was worth (we all want to feel worthwhile).

It never occurred to me that some of the highly favorable responses were based on little more than political factors: like a military service seeing the Bomb as a way to sell its own merchandise, or as a way to denigrate the merchandise of another service competing for funding in some operational area, or as a way to enhance one's position on a domestic political issue. It also never occurred to me that some of those people who were highly unfavorable of the N-bomb were being negative not so much because of an ingrained resistance to the concept, but rather because it threatened their merchandise or because their political enemies were for it.

This is not to say that there were not a significant number of people on the Washington scene who were able to rise above politics and accept, or reject for that matter, the Bomb on the basis of their own personal beliefs on national security. In fact, I would say that I met many more in the second category than in the first. The trouble, however, was that the political influence of this second group was much less than that of the first. A sad observation to make on a subject, our national security, which ought to be completely free of political finagling; but, I'm afraid, a fairly accurate one.

This situation hasn't changed very much since that time. In fact, I suspect it's gotten even worse, the reason being that the politics of nuclear weapons have become far more intense and emotional since the late 1950's.

At that time the populace and the government found nuclear weapons to be more acceptable than they do today. Nuclear weapons were officially regarded as the backbone of our defense. It was made very clear that except for very low-level conflicts (called "brush fire" wars in those days), any Communist aggression of respectable proportions would draw a U.S. nuclear response. Dwight Eisenhower had declared in 1955: "Where these things are used on strictly military targets and for strictly military purposes, I see no reason why they shouldn't be used just exactly as you would use a bullet or anything else."

In today's political climate, however, the opponents of nuclear weapons argue that their use should be avoided at practically all cost. There is an enormous political difference between killing enemy soldiers with neutrons and killing them with bullets. Jimmy Carter, writing about the use of tactical nuclear weapons and particularly neutron bombs in 1977, declared: "A decision to cross the nuclear threshold would be the most agonizing decision to be made by any President." Defense Secretary Caspar Weinberger said in 1981 that "our nuclear arsenal need never be employed to block aggression by conventional warfare [i.e., "bullets"] if our conventional defenses are sufficiently strong." This expression of current nuclear policy makes one wonder how much of the decision to produce N-bombs was based on politics and how much was based on a belief that these weapons would be genuinely useful. With nuclear weapons, especially tactical nuclear weapons, being as unpopular as they are these days, I would suspect that politics dominated the show.

Back to my story.

In February 1959 Jack Morse and I went to see Admiral Moorer. I performed my song-and-dance act. Moorer almost performed cartwheels. In short order he rounded up just about every admiral in the Pentagon for N-bomb briefings. I decided to add a Livermore scientist to the act, and give it a better ring of technical authenticity. Chuck McDonald, who was in charge of the two conceptual efforts originally exposed to me, consented to come aboard.

We quickly moved through the top navy circles, drawing full enthusiasm all the way. Probably the most enthusiastic was Admiral Hayward, who sat through the briefing several times. Finally I told him: "Look, Chick, you know the navy far better than I do. Why don't you give the briefing. You've heard it enough times to have it memorized." He demurred.

For its own reasons (mainly parochial, I suspect), the navy

began to push the Bomb and the briefing before other elements of the Pentagon and, whenever possible, to officials basically sympathetic to its cause. The N-bomb concept began to catch on. More and more people and agencies received the briefing.* Those who hadn't heard it now wanted to. And inevitably the word about the briefings got out to the press.

It never had occurred to me, either before or during this period, to pin some kind of identifying appellation on the Bomb. When describing the two explosive concepts, I simply referred to them by their code names, Dove and Starling. (At that time Livermore seemed to have an avian hangup over certain of their developments; the place was practically flapping.) The first time I recall seeing the term "neutron bomb" was in *U.S. News and World Report.* This was in May 1959, when the magazine revealed that the U.S. was working on a "neutron 'death ray' bomb which would kill man with streams of poisonous radiation, while leaving machines and buildings undamaged."

By now the air force had become uncomfortably aware of the navy-sponsored promotional effort. It was brought to the attention of General LeMay, who had left SAC to come to the Pentagon as Air Force Vice-Chief of Staff. LeMay decided that he ought to hear firsthand what I was telling everyone else. I received a call from an air force general, whom I knew personally and had dealt with professionally, telling me to get my charts together to brief LeMay.

At this time LeMay was a living legend. A great strategist and combat hero of World War II, who had put together the Strategic Air Command practically single-handedly. He was idolized all

* For reasons of academic competition, the concept never did catch on at RAND, which was far more a campus department than an objective think tank. (If one wished to conquer the world outside of RAND, one had to go outside of RAND, which is exactly what I wound up doing—along with other RANDites who were determined to push their products.) However, I did find out that a good-looking blonde down the hall had expressed interest in hearing my briefing. I took my charts down to her office, closed the door (not for lascivious reasons, but rather because I felt a little silly giving a briefing to one person) and gave her the full treatment. She seemed, or at least professed, to be interested. So, some months later I married her. From that time on her interest in my nefarious nuclear activities has been approximately zero, perhaps a little less.

over the country. Congressmen and senators were willing to give him almost anything he asked for. Within the ranks of the air force he was widely respected and undoubtedly even more widely feared. At least in the line of business, his behavior was gruff and taciturn. Enhancing his image was his habit of having a cigar in his mouth, usually unlit. Needless to say, this won him the sobriquet "the Cigar."*

When I was ushered into LeMay's office by the general who had called me, the Cigar was seated behind his desk, cigar in mouth. He made no motion of greeting, leaving me wondering what to do next. This was solved by my host officer, who suggested that I get started. For the next forty-five minutes I went through the briefing charts. LeMay sat motionless, cigar in mouth. Finally I finished. Still no movement from LeMay. No questions. Nothing. I stood there awkwardly until my host thanked LeMay, pointed to my charts for me to pick up and led me out of the office. Like the proverbial raven, the Cigar remained sitting, never flitting, for how long after, I have no idea.

Soon after that I got a call from my host general asking me to come to his office. With great embarrassment he explained to me that LeMay wanted the N-bomb show stopped. There were to be no more briefings. And I was really faced with a dilemma.

On the one hand, there was my job. RAND got its money from the air force, and the air force was LeMay. If I were to buck LeMay's order, I might very well find myself looking for another job. And I really liked my job. RAND was a great place to work. On the other hand, I was beginning to believe (incorrectly, as it turned out) that I was up to something really important unto itself and I sure as heck didn't want to be turned off now. I weighed

* In 1953 I came to SAC headquarters to visit with one of LeMay's deputies. Like LeMay, he was a cigar smoker. I was hoping to get some information important to a study I was doing. To enhance my prospects for getting this data, before coming to his office I'd stopped by a tobacconist and bought a half-dozen or so Cuban cigars for about a buck apiece. In those days this meant a damned good cigar. I walked into the deputy's office, reached into my pocket, took out a couple of cigars and offered them to him: "Have a couple of cigars, Zim." I was ignored. Instead of happily accepting them, Zim opened a desk drawer, brought out a box of cigars, opened it and said: "Here, Sam, have some of these. General LeMay smokes them." I got the message: When at SAC, do as LeMay does. They were vile cigars, at least compared with those I had anticipated smoking with Zim. I never made that mistake again.

these dismal prospects in my mind and decided that I wasn't going to become a martyr. I would capitulate, but I wanted the terms of capitulation to be formalized. In standard military fashion (which I'd learned about from my army days), I wanted a written order. I told the general: "Pinky, you get LeMay's order typed up on official air force stationery, mail it to me and I'll stop."

Now poor Pinky, a friend of mine, had his dilemma to wrestle over. If he mailed a stop order to me, he risked having it disclosed (like to the navy) and there might be all hell to pay. But if he decided not to take this risk, there was another risk, horror of horrors: the wrath of LeMay, which was probably the most wrathful in the U.S. military.

Pinky sat there staring into space, mulling over his dilemma. Finally he sighed, turned to me, swallowed hard and made a proposition. "How about this? You can go on with your briefings, but only in the Pentagon. You are not to talk outside this building. Furthermore, when you do talk, you are to preface your briefing with remarks to the effect that what you are presenting is purely technical. You are not giving a military endorsement of the technical concept." In other words, he wanted me to give a disclaimer that would make the air force less uncomfortable about the matter. This exceeded my threshold of personal pragmatism and I explained that he couldn't expect me to appear to be openly at odds with myself when I wasn't.

Again, poor Pinky sighed and backed away. "Okay, go ahead. But try not to say anything to get the air force mad."

The show went on, and as I continued with my spiel around the Pentagon, I noticed a familiar face cropping up in the audience time after time. It was an air force colonel who worked in the nuclear plans and policy shop. I knew him rather well. He had been assigned to check on me to make sure that the air force position wasn't being sandbagged—something I never had any intention of doing.

Right around that time, however, the air force tried to use me and the neutron bomb to sandbag the navy. I received a call from Hal Watson (Remember him? He was the air force colonel who had directed the first NATO tactical nuclear weapons study, in which I participated). By now Hal had become a major general. I was to come to his office to tell him and his staff about the Bomb. In the course of the briefing, I got around to giving the lethal range of the neutrons, which was pretty big: about one thousand yards. As soon as I showed this number, Watson jumped up and left the room. He headed right for the Chief of Staff's office, demanded to see the Chief immediately, and told him that he had just learned about a fantastic new weapon which symbolized the death knell of submarines. The Russians could make this weapon just as readily as we could, and use it to cook, with neutrons, the poor U.S. Navy submarine crews.

The Chief apparently didn't bother to check on what Watson had told him, and seemed to accept at face value this startling revelation. With that, Watson charged, spreading the word around the building that the navy's nuclear-powered Polaris missile submarines—competitors of SAC—were going to be doomed by neutron weapons. Among others who got the word was Admiral Hyman Rickover, the Father of the Nuclear Submarine. Rickover was enraged and issued a vehement denunciation of ME, not Watson. His rage was more than justified. The neutron range Watson was peddling was for air bursts. In water, where submarines are supposed to be, the range would be only several feet.

I could not take it into my heart to be enraged with Watson. Away from the air force, he was a pretty nice guy, who spent much of his time working for the treatment of mentally retarded children. In the Pentagon though, he was just one of a number of scalawags who would do almost anything to sabotage a rival service.

The Pentagon was now open territory, and the navy was still the only service affected by neutron fever. Admiral Moorer proceeded to push the Bomb to the top, which just so happened to be occupied by key figures close to the navy. In June 1959 Moorer arranged for the briefing to be given to a group that included the Secretary of Defense (Thomas Gates, who had moved up from Secretary of the Navy) and the acting Chairman of the Joint Chiefs of Staff (Admiral Arthur Radford). Most impressed with the concept was Radford, who as Chairman from 1953 to 1957 had been instrumental in the formulation of the Eisenhower administration's nuclear policies. Radford's basic view of nuclear weapons was that they "should be utilized simply as a new form of explosive." (There is no way to reconcile this statement with the Eisenhower policy of nuclear arms control; it is simply one of the typical conflicts of our government.)

Radford had been in favor of the United States coming to France's assistance in the first war in Indochina, recommending that nuclear weapons be provided if deemed necessary to prevent defeat. He had been dispatched to England to attempt to secure British acquiescence to that provision. His mission failed. The French collapsed, and we all know about the end of that sad and sorry road—our own collapse in Vietnam.

How effective nuclear weapons of the early 1950's vintage might have been in backing up the French, we'll never know. Maybe Radford thought he knew. My own guess is that the Model-T weapons we then had in our arsenal in limited quantities wouldn't have come close to solving the problem of Ho Chi Minh's guerrilla tactics. On the other hand, upon hearing about the potential for neutron weapons at the briefing, there was no doubt in Radford's mind that he knew they would have been effective in Indochina. He left the conference room muttering, "If we'd only had these weapons to use at Dien Bien Phu." (We'll get around to discussing possibilities for N-bombs in low-level wars later.)

Up until my presentation to Gates, Radford and the others that day, I had behaved myself with great circumspection regarding the air force's request. The act had stayed in the Pentagon. But the navy, which knew of my quarantine, was not to be denied in its efforts to get the message around to wherever they thought it might help their cause. The question was where, outside the Pentagon, they might go to secure a request for the briefing that would make it impossible for the air force to keep me bottled up. The answer was, obviously, the White House. The contact in the White House who could implement the plan to spring me turned out to be the President's naval aide, Captain Peter Aurand. Pete, whom I'd known for years and who was not renowned for timidity or discretion, was invited (better yet, "planted") to sit in on the briefing to Gates and company. He showed up in full uniform.

The meeting over, Pete came up to me, grabbed my arm and said, "Come with me." Meaning that I was to accompany him to the White House. Before I could tell him that I was not allowed to leave the building, my other arm was grabbed by Larry Henderson, a RAND vice-president whom the air force had sent to the briefing to keep tabs on me. Henderson informed Aurand that I was staying put. For a moment I had the feeling that I was on a medieval rack and I was waiting to see which arm would come off first.

Not caring to waste his time in a tug of war over my body, Pete asked Henderson whether he would still object if Gates were to okay my leaving. Henderson said he didn't know. He would have to check with the air force. Pete said, "Fine, I'll check with Gates while you check with the air force." With that, he walked into the Secretary's office as if it were his own. A few minutes later he walked out and told Henderson it was okay with Gates. Henderson, who had apparently been told by the air force not to buck the Secretary's ruling but to try to come along with me so that he could report on my White House behavior, now begged Aurand for permission to come along. Pete couldn't have cared less. Henderson came.

We drove onto the White House grounds, got out and went down into the White House basement and into a small room that was to be Ike's operating headquarters in the event of war. A little while later, another presidential military aide walked in, Army Major John Eisenhower, Ike's son. John listened very intently, and when I'd finished, he asked me if I'd mind waiting there a bit.

A few minutes later he returned, looking disappointed, and explained what had happened. His dad, having a break in schedule and some time to himself, had decided to step outside to his putting green and relax for a while. When John got to his dad's office, Dad was outside putting, and that was that. Ike had made it very plain that short of a major crisis, he was not to be disturbed on the putting green. Just about the only thing that could have gummed up the operation had gummed it up. It was just as well, however, for reasons I'll get around to in a bit, except that I felt like a kid who had been told on Christmas Eve that Santa was going on vacation, probably to play golf.

The Potomac was now bridged, enabling me to evangelize on the other side of the river. Senior officials in the White House, the

State Department and the CIA were briefed. At this point, however, the Atomic Energy Commission did not seem interested in having the story. Why not? I'll venture a guess: more air force politics.

The air force, of course, was determined to suppress the N-bomb story. At that time, 1959, aided and abetted by the Eisenhower policy of massive retaliation, which was based on the concept of thermonuclear reprisal against major aggressors (which meant, mainly, unleashing SAC bombers), the Pentagon's instructions to the AEC for new weapon developments very heavily emphasized the production of "Big Bangs"—H-bombs. Tactical weapons development was downplayed, and the air force meant to keep it that way. And it just so happened that the two key figures on the AEC—the chairman and the general manager—had formerly been with the air force. The chairman had been undersecretary of the air force, and the general manager was a general who had occupied the Number 1 position on nuclear weapons development matters for the Joint Chiefs of Staff. It was obvious that these gentlemen did not want the AEC to get a tactical N-bomb bug in its ear. But Jack Morse, even though he worked for the chairman, was determined to see to it that the commission heard the story. Risking his job, which he resigned not too long afterward, he went to see one of the commissioners, John Graham, told him about what had been going on and recommended that he personally hear the briefing.

Graham, who as a commission member had full independence to decide what he wanted or didn't want to hear, bought Jack's recommendation. He also invited the rest of the commissioners to attend. All but the chairman, John McCone, accepted. A meeting was scheduled, and since Washington officialdom at this lofty level is extremely busy, or has to appear to be, the meeting was limited to twenty minutes. It lasted about two hours. The commissioners showed keen interest, and showered us with questions.

Dominating the discussion was Commissioner Willard Libby, who, having a Nobel Prize in chemistry under his belt for devising the radioactive-carbon-dating scheme, was best equipped to understand the technical material. Libby went hook, line and sinker for the N-bomb. He recommended that the AEC give highest priority to the work going on at Livermore. The other commissioners present agreed, and McCone, who found himself a possible minority of one out of five, decided to go along. And that's how the development of the N-bomb began. Two years later, when the nuclear test moratorium ended, the Livermore lab was ready to begin the actual testing of neutron warheads, which it proceeded to do early in 1962.

Since the AEC had full freedom to determine the course of its nuclear weapons research, the most important battle of the promotional campaign had been won when the commissioners decided to proceed. However, the commissioners deemed it necessary to get key members of the Congress to support the Bomb, particularly those belonging to the Joint Committee on Atomic Energy (JCAE), which oversaw AEC activities. A presentation to the JCAE was arranged. It turned out to be an utter debacle, because of some Washington politics of that moment that had nothing to do with nuclear weapons of any kind. It had to do with a long-standing and bitter feud between two powerful Washington personalities.

One of the feuders happened to be the chairman of the JCAE, Senator Clinton Anderson. The other was Lewis Strauss, who had served as Eisenhower's AEC chairman and at this time was seeking confirmation by the Senate to become Secretary of Commerce. The two were diametrically opposed on domestic politics and had been fighting for years. Unfortunately Anderson hated Strauss so much that he vowed to block his confirmation and seemed willing to stake his Senate career on this avowal. This meant that the senator was of a mood at this time not only to oppose Strauss personally, but practically anything or anybody who was linked to him. And since Strauss was closely linked to the Livermore laboratory (indeed, he had been instrumental in establishing the lab), and the lab was developing the N-bomb, Anderson was determined to be against the N-bomb—and me, whom he had never met or even heard about. This was what I was up against when I showed up before the committee, the day before the Senate vote on the Strauss confirmation.

It was the first time I'd ever appeared before a group of congressmen, or evem met one of them. My father used to tell me when I was a kid that they were all a bunch of crooks. So I wasn't prepared to like any of them, especially not Senator Anderson, who did about everything he possibly could to confirm my prejudice. He denounced the neutron bomb in scathing terms. It was a "capitalist bomb" (the first time I heard such a description). It was immoral, and so on. All during this time he was gulping down pills at a great rate. The questions he asked had little to do with the subject of the hearing. They were designed to bait me into saying something I shouldn't. This trap, however, I was able to avoid, by luck at first, by design later on.

I was so flabbergasted by the first few questions that I was practically paralyzed in trying to figure out how to answer them. But then I noticed something. If I didn't say something because I couldn't, one of the congressmen would say something. These guys were unable to keep quiet. So I made a point of hesitating after every question, and each time I was saved. I don't think I made one reply.

Anderson finally left, probably to use the time remaining to make sure his supporters for the next day's vote were staying in line. The rest of the hearing was little more than a shambles, thanks principally to Anderson's performance. Despite this, however, most of the committee members seemed to have been impressed and were favorably inclined toward the N-bomb. Looking back at this episode, I suspect they had come to the hearing favorably inclined—for reasons I'll get around to shortly.

The next day the Senate refused to confirm Strauss. Whereas this made Anderson practically orgasmic, Strauss must have been crushed. He had undergone a terrible humiliation. If he was crushed, however, it was not noticeable when Jack and I showed up the day after the vote to tell him about the N-bomb. He was jaunty, courteous, hospitable and downright charming. If way down deep he was churning over what had happened the day before, there was no way of knowing it. He paid rapt attention to the briefing and asked highly probing questions.

Finally it was time to go. Strauss had an appointment to keep. We left together, and as he went over to his wife to buss her good-bye, he told her, very reassuringly, "Don't worry, dear, I'll find work." Strauss, who needed a job like a hole in the head, had long ago become a millionaire tens of times over, which I knew. I tried desperately to suppress a guffaw and told myself: "There's a man."

Most important, Strauss was entranced with the N-bomb concept, genuinely so. He had no parochial ax to grind and took to the idea because he believed in it. He told us that he would do everything possible to support our program and would be in touch with us. From that time on I saw him frequently, and having meant what he said, he was of great help toward getting us together with people of influence.

Getting the AEC to order Livermore to give the N-bomb the highest priority represented a great victory. Yet it was only half the battle won. The other half involved the moratorium on nuclear testing. As it turned out, most of the champions of the neutron bomb were far more concerned with resuming nuclear testing than with acquiring discriminate tactical nuclear weapons. In fact, they were far more concerned with testing new thermonuclear weapons, in line with the ongoing massive retaliation strategy.

However, the Defense Department and the AEC were directly under the thumb of the President, so it would have been a pretty sporty course for these agencies to push openly for a resumption of testing, regardless of how persuasive they thought their reasons might be. But this was not so for the Congress or the press. And in pushing the N-bomb as the major argument for their case, they began a vigorous campaign to get testing going again. No matter. Ike refused to budge for the remainder of his term. However, our supporters succeeded in giving the Bomb a tremendous amount of publicity. They also succeeded in starting a debate over the N-bomb issue, in many ways similar to but hardly as violent as that which erupted in the summer of 1977, when it was revealed by *The Washington Post* that production had been authorized for neutron warheads to go into the army's Lance battlefield missile.

It was also *The Washington Post* that, in the summer of 1959, obtained highly classified information (another leak) and revealed the first definitive account of the development of the neutron bomb. In a front-page article on July 19, the *Post* revealed that "a radically new type of atomic weapon, which could have a profound effect on the cold war and international relations, is being discussed in military circles." This new weapon was described as "a bomb that would produce as much man-killing radiation as a large weapon, yet have the destructive blast of a small weapon and the radioactive fallout of an even smaller one. It is a bomb that would be capable of killing an enemy force without too much physical damage to an area and without the fallout that would make the region uninhabitable after the attack."

According to the *Post* article, there were two N-bomb efforts afoot, "under the nondescript project names Dove and Starling," at the Livermore laboratory.

Please allow me to backtrack briefly. What I neglected to mention earlier was that before I spoke at the JCAE briefing, John McCone arrived, fresh from having discussed the N-bomb with the President (and also fresh from having been briefed by me just before seeing the President). He requested permission to say a few words. What he wanted to impress upon the congressmen was the tremendous importance and sensitivity of this program. It was of the highest security classification and it was essential that security be kept. (Actually, the N-bomb did not have top security classification at that time. It was classified "secret, restricted data," which means that the classification was at the level of "secret" and that it involved nuclear weapons data.) So we get an idea how the President may have viewed the N-bomb—namely, as a threat to the nuclear-test-ban negotiations going on at that time.

Getting back to the *Post* article, this was exactly what the thrust of the article was all about:

> If such a weapon is possible, as it now appears to be, it may make attempts to set up a total nuclear test ban as a first step toward disarmament meaningless, since tests on large weapons of this type could be concealed underground. And the low-blast effect would make them difficult to detect . . . The need for further tests to perfect this type of bomb may have been responsible for some of the opposition to a total nuclear test ban now being discussed by the three nuclear powers, the United States, Great Britain and the Soviet Union, at Geneva . . . These tests will undoubtedly have an effect on the Geneva negotiations, since the U.S. delegation has already been informed of the Dove and Starling projects.

The *Post* article was an accurate condensation of my JCAE secret briefing. Naturally the administration was highly upset by this disclosure and ordered a full investigation to find the culprit who had blabbed to the *Post.* They never caught anyone. They practically never do.

On Capitol Hill a growing number of congressmen began to sound off against continuing the nuclear test moratorium—or even having a test ban at all. In this connection the N-bomb was mentioned most frequently. The congressmen argued that it was essential for U.S. security and that if we didn't get cracking on it, the Russians would beat us to the punch. In fact, they might already have done so, since underground N-bomb tests could not be detected.

In the forefront of this congressional coterie was Senator Thomas Dodd (D-Conn). To be more accurate, Dodd was lengths out in front of the pack, making the Bomb the focal point of an intense personal crusade. Dodd was an improbable combination of a domestic liberal (one of the staunchest champions of civil rights), while being a "hard-liner" on defense and a devout anti-Communist (this attitude undoubtedly having been shaped by his close association with J. Edgar Hoover when he was an FBI agent, and by his intense Catholicism). The senator had been contacted by someone who had heard about, or heard, the N-bomb briefing, and who convinced him that this was an important matter. Dodd took the bait. In May 1960 he issued a major speech on the Senate floor attacking Eisenhower's test-ban position. He brought up the neutron bomb, his knowledge of which was supposedly based on press reports, in his speech:

> . . . Although there have been a few fragmentary references to the neutron bomb in the press, I was told, when I tried to obtain more information, that the matter was classified. When I pressed my physicist friend further, he threw up his hands in despair and said: "You must forgive me. I have never heard of a neutron."
>
> I consider all the hush-hush that surrounds the neutron bomb to be a glaring instance of the official abuse of secrecy. To keep the facts of life on the Nuclear Age from the American people is foolish and potentially disastrous. If there is possibility that a neutron bomb can be built, if there appears to be any chance that the Soviets may suc-

> ceed in building one before we do, then the American people have a right to the facts.
>
> I believe President Eisenhower owes a similar duty to the American people in the case of the neutron bomb. The President should tell the people what the scientists told him. Not to do so would be a dereliction that can only lead to the most dangerous kind of speculation.

If Eisenhower became aware of Dodd's plea for him to tell the people about the Bomb—and it would have been difficult for him not to be aware, since the speech was picked up by the press all over the country—he certainly was not moved by it. There was never official mention of the neutron bomb by the White House during his stay in office. Regarding Dodd's demand that Ike tell the people what the scientists told him, who were these scientists? Thanks to golf, I wasn't one of them. Nor was any member of the Livermore lab, or to the best of my knowledge anyone from the AEC or the Pentagon. If, as Dodd implied, Ike had been briefed by some scientists, it probably transpired through his science advisor, Dr. George Kistiakowsky.

As a renowned scientist from Harvard, Kistiakowsky had played a key role at Los Alamos during the war. The trouble was that although he had impeccable scientific credentials, as did most influential members of the U.S. scientific community, many of whom were government consultants and members of the President's Science Advisory Committee, he also had a strong ideological conviction that a nuclear test ban was imperative. As such, he couldn't have been expected to look kindly upon the N-bomb, nor could he have been expected to give it high marks before the President.

I had gone to the White House to brief Kistiakowsky around the time of Dodd's speech. At no time during the briefing did he have any technical quarrels with me. Actually he found the technical description quite intriguing. However, he made his political objections very plain, and they were precisely those expressed by the two Cal Tech scientists who were presented with my ideas for using tactical nuclear weapons in Korea. Were we to use neutron bombs in Asia, and it was essentially in this context that I described the weapon's military potential, the Asian condemnation of this act would result in political disaster for the U.S.

I don't know whether Kistiakowsky actually advised Eisenhower on the N-bomb. At the time nobody told me if he did. Almost twenty years later, however, with about 20/1000 hindsight, at a press conference in Cambridge in April 1978, he said that he considered the weapon unfeasible and that he regarded the claim that it would limit harm to civilians as dishonest. Moreover, he claimed that President Eisenhower had killed the project on his recommendation. Strange that the killing took place at about the same time that the project had been given top priority and was going like gangbusters at Livermore.

From the very beginning of the neutron bomb saga there has been one thing that particularly impressed—better yet, depressed—me about most renowned American scientists. This is their ability to be impeccably careful and responsible when working in their fields of specialization (if they're not, their colleagues will catch them and even punish them) but their sloppiness and irresponsibility when giving their scientific opinion on nuclear weapons when they have an ideological bias against them, because they know that their colleagues, who share their bias, don't give a damn when they do this.

Kistiakowsky and many of his scientific colleagues have gotten away with murder in their attacks on the neutron bomb, especially over the past few years while the battle over production has been for real. (I'll pick up some of these guys and the errors of their ways later on.) During this time the scientific community has stood on the sidelines and let them go on undisputed. So has the U.S. Defense Department, including, for example, Carter's Secretary of Defense, Harold Brown, who publicly urged that neutron warheads be produced and deployed, and yet did not put out one official document refuting the outrageous technical claims made against it by his fellow scientists.

Harold, a brilliant nuclear physicist who had been director of the Livermore laboratory when the N-bomb effort first got moving, had at that time expressed his great gratitude to me for what I was doing. To have become director, he obviously had to have considerable knowledge and experience in all aspects of nuclear weapons, which he sure as heck did. He knew all the technical facts about the neutron bomb then, and still did when he took over the Pentagon in 1977.

While Defense Secretary, Harold was quick to do open battle

with anyone who made technically slipshod statements with regard to SALT II, the cruise missile, the MX "racetrack" system, and what have you. And yet he sat in that job for more than three years without once bothering to respond to attacks on the neutron bomb by fellow scientists, many of whom, including Kistiakowsky, he had known long and well. It was as though the Carter administration never did want the Bomb, although while these scientists were attacking it, they claimed they did.

After Senator Dodd had given his test-ban speech and he had noticed the big stir his neutron bomb remarks caused in the press and among fellow congressmen, he decided that he ought to get the story straight from the horse's mouth. He had Jack Morse contact me, requesting that I come to his office and tell him about the Bomb. Not having forgotten my father's warnings about politicians, I told Jack that I wasn't interested. If Dodd wanted to see me, he would have to go through proper security channels. Jack was aghast that I could turn down a U.S. senator that way, but nevertheless he told Dodd of my decision.

Under a Republican administration, which Dodd was vehemently attacking, permission was not about to be granted. The senator had to wait until Kennedy was elected. It was not until Kennedy was installed in office that I was given permission to go up to the Hill to brief the senator.

Dodd was extremely receptive, although I suspect that he had already made up his mind to be receptive. Now he felt qualified to recommend the briefing to his senatorial colleagues, and attempted to do so. However, there was a roadblock in his way. The JCAE, which for its own parochial reasons wanted to keep the nuclear weapons business in the Congress to itself. What Dodd was able to do though, was to call some senators on the JCAE who either hadn't been present when I briefed the committee or, because of Anderson's irascibility, had never had the opportunity to find out what it was all about. To say that I actually gave (or was allowed to give) the briefing in any coherent form would be considerably at odds with the facts of the occasion.

One of the senators whom Dodd convinced to hear me out was, of all people, Clinton Anderson. I was told to meet Anderson outside a Senate conference room where the Agriculture Committee, which he chaired, was in session. I figured that we would go to his office, close the door and then get around to my presentation. But that was not to be.

Long after I arrived, the senator came out, recognized me sitting there and explained that the session was going long past the originally planned time. He had called a break for ten or fifteen minutes. Could I quickly tell him about the Bomb—right there? I started to explain that this was secret material, there were scads of uncleared people milling around, and couldn't we go to a secure area? He told me that there wasn't time for that. "Let's go into the corner of the room and have your charts face the wall so nobody can see," he suggested. "And keep your voice down." If God wants to discuss secrets with you in a crowded anteroom, well, you discuss secrets in a crowded anteroom.

In contrast to his previous behavior, Anderson was fully attentive, and downright gracious. When we were through, he smiled almost bashfully and apologized profusely for his previous conduct. I accepted his apology. Thank God he didn't know that I had begun a friendship with Lewis Strauss!

One ally of Senator Dodd was Thomas Murray, who had been an AEC commissioner from 1950 to 1957. Like Dodd, Murray was a devout Catholic and very active and influential in U.S. Catholic circles. While with the AEC, he had become intensely concerned with the moral aspects of nuclear weapons. So obsessed was he with these moral concerns, that he became known as "the conscience" of the AEC.

Like Oppenheimer, Murray regarded a nuclear policy based on the bombing of cities as grossly immoral. Holding to this view, in accordance with his Catholic conscience, he developed an unyielding belief that the West should stake out its defense against communism on the ground, using discriminate tactical nuclear weapons. While on the commission, he had pressed hard for giving greater research priorities to these weapons. When he left the commission, he became a consultant to the JCAE, using this appointment to continue his struggle to promote his moral views.

While Murray was a commissioner, he had gotten to know Jack Morse. They both held the same fervent beliefs on the necessity of attaining a discriminate tactical nuclear capability, and they became friends and partners in a common cause.

In 1959, when my neutron bomb activities were confined to the

Pentagon, Jack pulled a fast one. I was scheduled to brief an Assistant Secretary of Defense (arranged for, naturally, by the navy). When I came into the Secretary's office, there was Murray. What had happened was that Jack had contacted Murray, who was in the habit of making frequent visits to the Pentagon, and told him to drop into the Secretary's office. Whereas Murray's presence constituted a technical violation of my promise (as did Aurand's), strictly speaking I was conforming to the air force edict. When the briefing was over, I had gained a tremendously dedicated supporter and a friend as well. In his own quiet way Murray began to lobby for the neutron bomb, in classified circles, of course.

In the fall of 1960, a presidential election year, Murray decided to go public with his lobbying. He also decided to start at the top. Immediately before the election he wrote an open letter to presidential candidates Nixon and Kennedy, wherein he stated his reasons for the need to develop N-bombs and the concomitant necessity for the U.S. to terminate the existing test moratorium. He also gave strategic and moral reasons as to why developing the neutron bomb was imperative for the United States.

Murray wrote:

> The [neutron bomb] will not be a larger and more efficient H-bomb, nor a smaller and more efficient A-bomb. It will be a weapon of a different category. All that may be said of it here is that it is primarily antipersonnel in destruction and effect. Hence, it is apt for proper military uses. It lends itself to a new type of nuclear strategy that would be more narrowly military in character. And it need not create suicidal hazards for the country that employs it. Therefore, a moral argument for the use of the new weapon is possible, as it generally is not possible in the case of the immense weapons of sheer mass-destruction . . .

He went on to say: "Conceptual designs for this new type of weapon have existed in American laboratories. They would have already been tested, had it not been for our test moratorium. The moratorium has effectively blocked American advance to a new position of military and political strength." And he sounded the tocsin about the possibility that the Soviets might get the neutron bomb by testing clandestinely during the moratorium: "I take it for granted that the Soviet Union is actively developing nuclear technology along this revolutionary line. I must assume that they have done some preliminary tests of the new 'fantastic' weapon. Such tests could easily have been carried out without detection."

Murray's effort to get the N-bomb into the presidential debate failed. Neither candidate ever brought it up. On the other hand, if there was no response from the candidates, there was an instant response from the scientists, including members of Eisenhower's Science Advisory Committee.

One of them, Jerome Wiesner of MIT (who was actively campaigning for Kennedy, and soon would be his science advisor in the White House), blasted Murray as "irresponsible." Said Wiesner: "I know of no reason for resuming testing immediately. My own view is that the United States cannot let any single thing hinder the [test-ban] negotiations. The use or leak of 'scare' stories inhibits the government in such talks."

Another member, Isador Rabi of Columbia (who had won the Nobel Prize for his work in nuclear physics), belittled Murray on technical grounds. "Mr. Murray does not know very much about atomic physics and is technically not qualified to discuss such questions," he declared. However, he could not discuss why Murray was off-base, because secrecy prevented him "from discussing these questions freely."

As for the Eisenhower administration's position on the N-bomb, I think it's clear that except for a parochial desire on the part of the AEC to continue testing and developing nuclear weapons, there never was any serious interest in acquiring the Bomb. Even if there had been a determined attempt in the government to establish requirements for the weapon, it would have gone for naught. The President would have killed it. The Pentagon was pushing the neutron bomb for parochial service reasons, and in an attempt to push the President into terminating the test moratorium so they could develop the weapons they really wanted—and which the White House would go along with.

Ike was primarily for developing hydrogen bombs. That's what his nuclear policies were all about. He had no interest in any kind of tactical nuclear weapons, although he probably would have authorized their use had war broken out. He was willing to go along with service requests for such weapons to keep peace among warring military factions. But at no time during his administration did the services put in serious requirements for discriminate weapons. Finally Ike was not going to let any device like the neutron bomb interfere with his aspirations for a nuclear test ban. Nor were his White House scientific advisors about to let him get any such ideas.

Ike's policies were based primarily on the use of thermonuclear weapons. He certainly wouldn't have tolerated the nuclear test moratorium as long as he did if he had thought that in so doing he would have jeopardized U.S. strategic nuclear superiority. Yet that's exactly what happened. The Russians broke the moratorium in 1961, with the most massive series of tests the world has ever seen, and pulled ahead of the U.S. in high-yield thermonuclear weapons technology.

CHAPTER 3
THE NEUTRON BOMB WAS DEAD, OR SO IT SEEMED

ON NOVEMBER 8, 1960, by the thinnest of margins, Senator John Kennedy was elected President. Knowingly or otherwise (with *otherwise* having by far the highest probability), the citizens of the United States had voted for a profound policy change in national security. This change was in the direction, as the new President described it, of putting the nuclear genie back into the bottle. Ground wars were to be fought with conventional weapons, to avoid, to the extent possible, the use of tactical nuclear weapons.

The theory behind the decision was that the introduction of tactical nuclear weapons on the battlefield would set into motion an inexorable train of events which would end with the mutual extinction of the United States and the Soviet Union. We needed a middle option, as Kennedy put it, to avoid the unacceptable extremes of "humiliation or all-out nuclear action." As a senator, Kennedy had explained the consequences of using tactical nuclear weapons: "Inevitably the use of small nuclear armaments will lead to larger and larger nuclear armaments on both sides, until the worldwide holocaust has begun."

With such an apocalyptic view of tactical nuclear weapons, the neutron bomb suddenly was really on the outside looking in.

Ike didn't like the N-bomb because he was going to bomb the hell out of the Soviet Union if they started a ground war against a major ally of ours. This thermonuclear threat, he was convinced, would serve to deter any Soviet aggression at all. The hydrogen bomb was regarded as the deterrence bomb. Any other kind of bomb was inconsequential.

Kennedy didn't like the N-bomb because he was scared to death that it would lead to a trading of thermonuclear strikes, and that the Russians' thermonuclear capability had become so terrifying that this was one trade that would do us in. He was only half correct, but still a lot more correct than Eisenhower, who had stubbornly stuck with a doctrine that was becoming increasingly more dangerous, as the Russians increased their thermonuclear capabilities by the day. Kennedy was dangerously incorrect in assuming that the Soviet policy would eschew the use of tactical nuclear weapons as his policy would.

We'll get around to the Kennedy nuclear policies later on, primarily because they have not passed into oblivion and are more dominating today than ever. And we'll explain what a continuation of these policies means to America. But in the meantime we should get back on the neutron bomb track and to what happened to the Bomb with the installation of a new President.

Shortly after the election Senator Dodd called Jack Morse, now a private citizen living in California, and asked if it would be okay for him to write to the President-elect suggesting that he hear the briefing. This was fine with Jack, who then checked with me.

Great with me! Not only does one gasp with anticipation at meeting a guy about to become President, but I had voted for him, expecting far better from him than Nixon, who would have been burdened with the Eisenhower policies—at least at the beginning. What a thrill to meet a President of my choice. No objections from Jack and me, Dodd wrote to Kennedy. I'm inserting into the text a draft of his letter (which his son Christopher Dodd, now a U.S. senator from the great state of Connecticut, so kindly got out of his father's personal files for me).

November 25, 1960

The Honorable John F. Kennedy
Old Senate Office Building
Room 362
Washington, D.C.

Dear Mr. President:

My warm thanks for your very gracious note of November 22. I am all the more grateful for it because I have some inkling of how busy you must be.

Because I am aware of the great demands now on your time, I have in general hesitated to write to you. If I now take the liberty of writing to you personally, it is because I consider the matter I here outline to be of the gravest importance.

A press report a week or so ago implied that you were in contact with or were receiving briefings from a group of nuclear scientists who are generally skeptical about the possibility and potential of the neutron bomb and of other possible developments in the field of nuclear weapons technology.

I have no way of knowing whether this story was accurate. I am nevertheless worried by the fact that those scientists who question the neutron bomb or belittle its importance, have been making public and vociferous statements—while those scientists who believe that it is possible and who have, in fact, done important work in this area, have been unable to say anything for reasons of security. Inevitably this has resulted in a one-sided presentation.

This is one of those situations where men of integrity and unquestioned ability can take diametrically opposed points of view. In the course of preparing my speech on "The Eight Fallacies of the Nuclear Test Ban," I heard on excellent authority that there were top-notch men who not merely consider the neutron bomb a possibility but who believe it is no further away technologically than the H Bomb was six months before it was developed. They also believe that it would have a revolutionary military impact in the limited war field and in the development of the anti-missile-missile.

Which side is one to believe? Obviously both sides must be heard. As a non-expert, I myself have an open mind, but as a general rule I believe history proves that those who say "we must and we can" have been right far more often than those who say "we should not and we cannot." As a reminder from the recent past, I would point out that only a year before we exploded our first H Bomb, Hans Bethe and other opponents of the H Bomb, were saying—in almost these words—"It cannot be made, and it should not be made."

From everything that I know about you, I am certain that you would want to expose yourself to both points of view on the neutron bomb; and I know, too, that you would want the American people to have both points of view on an issue that may conceivably involve the survival of the free world. If the matter of the H Bomb had not been publicly raised by Joseph Alsop and others, President Truman might have found it much more difficult to overcome the opposition to it.

It is in this light that I wish to submit a proposal for your consideration.

It has recently come to my attention that a two man team consisting of a former assistant to Atomic Energy Commissioner McCone and a nuclear physicist associated with the US Government has given a series of briefings on the technological feasibility and military applications of the neutron bomb to groups of top-ranking Pentagon officers and to scientists and officials of the Atomic Energy Commission. Their audiences included the scientists in the AEC concerned with this specific area of weapons development and officers of the armed forces concerned with the military evaluation of these weapons. According to everything I have heard, these briefings made a tremendous impression.

If my information is correct, in consequence of these briefings the Department of Defense has now established a very high priority on the development of these weapons.

If you can manage a half hour sometime before the Inauguration, I know that the same team of experts, who so impressed the Pentagon, would be happy to meet with you at your convenience. I cannot mention names here for understandable reasons, but if you are interested, I shall come to see you wherever you may be at the time, with a view to setting up this meeting. I am leaving for Europe on Tuesday, November 28. I shall be back home and at your disposal, however, after December 15.

It was a great fight, it was a great privilege campaigning for you—and I believe that in you the Democratic Party has again given the United States a President who will set his stamp upon history.

With best wishes,

Sincerely yours,

THOMAS J. DODD

TJD:mc

Kennedy did not pick up Dodd's suggestion to get the briefing, although he did respond to his letter and promised to look into the matter personally. Indeed, very shortly after coming into the White House, Kennedy visited AEC headquarters to be educated on nuclear matters by the new management. At that time he did bring up the neutron bomb. However, with his own ideology about tactical nuclear weapons now having taken hold in the administration, he wasn't about to be told that it was the greatest thing since sliced bread. He wasn't.

With this unenthusiastic report by the AEC, Kennedy's direct interest in the neutron bomb faded quickly. Although attempts were made to move my briefing through his White House circle of national security advisors to his immediate attention, they were all unsuccessful. One of Kennedy's military aides had me write a condensation of the briefing, which he passed on to Kennedy while the President was getting dressed one morning. Kennedy read it, so his aide told me, but apparently already had his mind made up and was not swayed by what I wrote.

* * *

Although Kennedy may have preferred to forget about the neutron bomb and focus his attention more on his real goal for U.S. battlefield capabilities—a substantial buildup of conventional forces—his preference was denied to him by an increasing chorus of demands that he resume nuclear testing. In the Congress the prime mover in this direction continued to be Senator Dodd.

In March of 1961 Dodd finally got around to getting permission for me to brief him on the neutron bomb. With that under his belt, he decided to have another go at President Kennedy. A couple of weeks later he wrote to the President again, urging that he hear what I had to say.

The letter was formally dispatched by Dodd's office, arrived at the White House and, like all letters directed to the President, entered the "System." Coming from a U.S. senator, this one did rather well. It went all the way to the office of the President's assistant for national security before it was pigeonholed. Not getting a response from Kennedy, Dodd checked into the delay and found out what had happened. There was nothing he could do but try again. It just so happened that Dodd was on good terms with the President's brother Robert, then the attorney general. So this time Dodd hand-delivered it to Bobby, who in turn hand-delivered it to the President. Still nothing happened. The White House had become a stone wall.

Shortly before Dodd wrote to the President, I had gone to the White House to brief Kennedy's national security advisor, McGeorge Bundy. I arrived, charts in hand, and was told by Bundy that I had but five or ten minutes to deliver the briefing. He was terribly busy and besides he'd already been told about it and thought he knew what it was all about. There was no time for charts, and speaking very rapidly, I began an encapsulated description of the subject. Almost immediately Bundy interrupted with a question. I told him that I could answer best by showing him one of the charts, which I did. More than an hour later, I had gone through the last chart, and Bundy said that he now really did understand what the Bomb was. But he saw no need for such weapons. I asked him why he felt that way. His response was that if we had to use nuclear weapons to stop the Red Army from taking over Europe, he would favor hitting them with the biggest weapons we had. My riposte was: "On our allies' soil?" He didn't reply. He couldn't have. He had gotten the point. That ended the meeting.

April 7, 1961

The President,
The White House,
Washington, D.C.

Dear Mr. President: PERSONAL—SECRET

In view of the interest you expressed in your letter of March 6th, after you had received your first briefing on the neutron bomb, I am taking the liberty of writing to you again.

In your letter you said that you plan to obtain additional information on this development so that you would be "in a position to evaluate its actual military significance." The specific purpose of this letter is to suggest that you might find it advantageous personally to receive the very carefully prepared neutron bomb briefing that Mr. Sam Cohen, Rand Corporation physicist, has recently given to top Defense Department officials and to key members of the Joint Committee on Atomic Energy.

There are other people who know something about the neutron bomb and who have made presentations on the subject to the Joint Committee on Atomic Energy, the Atomic Energy Commission, and the Pentagon. But because he originated the concept and has done the most thinking about it, Sam Cohen is uniquely qualified to present the matter comprehensively, with particular emphasis on the evaluation of its actual military significance.

I had heard about the neutron bomb in a general way from several sources and in my Senate speech of last May 12th, I had spoken about it as one of the most serious technological possibilities on the horizon.

Because of my interest, I recently asked the Rand Corporation and the Department of Defense for permission to hear Mr. Cohen's briefing on the neutron bomb. I received this briefing just over two weeks ago. (Mr. Cohen was accompanied by Captain John H. Morse, Jr., former Special Assistant to Mr. McCone, who participated in the briefing.)

I cannot possibly do justice to their presentation. Mr. Cohen made me realize how incomplete my own knowledge of the neutron bomb had been up until that moment, how much greater its significance is than I had realized. I was more than ever convinced that on the single issue of the neutron bomb might hang the survival of the Free World.

It was Mr. Cohen's belief that, while the members of the Joint Committee were aware of the neutron bomb, a good deal of what he had to say was unknown both to the members of the Committee and to key members of the Department of Defense. Because of this, I checked with General Loper's office to make certain that the Department of Defense had no objection, and I then arranged a series of individual meetings with Senator Pastore, Senator Anderson, Congressman Price and Congressman Holifield. From everything that I have heard, they all felt that they had learned far more from Mr. Cohen's briefing than from any previous briefings on the subject.

Mr. Cohen's presence in Washington last week had a cumulative impact that we had not reckoned on. Within a matter of days, the initial briefing he had given to members of the Joint Committee and to Pentagon officials, led to briefings of General Lemnitzer, Secretary McNamara, Dr. Bundy and Dr. Rostow. This, I think, provides some measure of the great impression Mr. Cohen made on those who heard him.

Before writing this letter, I hesitated for some time because of my appreciation of the incredible demands upon your time and because of my reluctance to impose upon you further. But this is a matter of such critical importance that I presume to ask you to give Mr. Cohen thirty minutes to make his presentation. I know you will find it worthwhile.

With every best wish,

Sincerely yours,

THOMAS J. DODD

TJD:mw

Still another White House occupant I saw was General Maxwell Taylor, a hero of World War II and Korea, who had resigned as

Army Chief of Staff in protest over the Eisenhower defense policies. Taylor had come aboard as a military advisor to the President, stayed on for a short while in this capacity and then moved over to the Pentagon as Chairman of the JCS. The general seemed genuinely impressed with the Bomb. He thought that the effort ought to go on at top priority, and asked me to check on Washington's official interest in the N-bomb development. Would I please report to him if the interest seemed to be slipping. As soon as the nuclear test moratorium ended in September 1961, the slippage began. I dutifully got hold of his executive officer, told him what was going on and that it had been Taylor's request that I apprise him of the situation. The exec said he would relay this to the general and get back to me about my reporting to him. He never did. And to the best of my knowledge, Taylor did nothing of significance toward getting the JCS to establish requirements for the neutron bomb when he became Chairman.

Another senator whom Dodd contacted was Henry "Scoop" Jackson (D-Wash.), who at that time was chairman of the JCAE's Subcommittee on Military Applications. Jackson had not been present at the 1959 JCAE presentation. Jack Morse and I went to see him. He reacted favorably and instructed his assistant to set up hearings before his subcommittee as soon as possible. Several weeks later the hearings took place. Again I was asked to testify, but this time I did so in the company of a broad spectrum of senior officials concerned with nuclear weapons matters. Included in this august company was the JCS Chairman, the Pentagon's R&D chief (Harold Brown, who had just left Livermore) and the service R&D chiefs, and the new chairman of the AEC, Glen Seaborg.

All those testifying from the Defense Department were full of glowing praise for neutron weapons, even the air force representative. This was understandable. At this juncture the Pentagon was in full court press on trying to force the test moratorium to an end. Any means to this end were more than justifiable, and this included an air force willingness to join in a common cause to achieve a unified position on the neutron bomb in the Pentagon. I might add that if any single thing is responsible for my skepticism about how Washington deals with our nation's military security, this is it. At this time I learned from the air force colonel, who had been instructed to keep tabs on what I said in my briefings, that LeMay had called him and some other officers into his office to plot strategy on the moratorium. During the plotting LeMay asked whether the air force couldn't use the neutron bomb as a reason for terminating the moratorium. When I heard this, I felt ill.

Anyway, after the Pentagon contingent was through, Seaborg and I were called to the table. Naturally Seaborg drew the majority of the questioning, most of which he very adroitly sidestepped. It was obvious, knowing how the congressmen felt, that he didn't want to say anything deprecatory about the Bomb. But it was also clear that he wasn't about to praise it. (Keep in mind that he was presiding over the AEC when Kennedy had visited there a few months earlier, at which time Kennedy was given an unenthusiastic picture of the weapon.) At one point Seaborg was asked about the danger of radioactivity produced by an N-bomb burst, such radioactivity would be caused by the absorption of neutrons in soil. He wouldn't answer, pleading that he hadn't had enough time to acquaint himself with this particular matter, and so on. I had to speak up and answer for him. And I was really furious inside at Seaborg's behavior. I was ticked off not because he was being evasive (any of the guys present were capable of doing that), but because I happened to know that Glen Seaborg was the holder of a Nobel Prize for his pioneering work in radiochemistry. Had he wanted to, he could have given Congress a dissertation on the matter.

Needless to say, the hearing was a success. Jackson and Representative Chet Holifield (D-Calif.) were sufficiently impressed (probably before they walked into the hearing) to dispatch a highly classified letter to the President, stressing the importance of the neutron bomb and its relationship to the test-moratorium issue. Nothing happened. Like Eisenhower before him, Kennedy seemed determined to keep the moratorium going, while accelerating efforts at Geneva to reach a comprehensive test-ban treaty with the Soviets.

The head of the Kennedy administration technical negotiating team at Geneva was James Fisk, a distinguished scientist and president (at that time) of the Bell Telephone Laboratories. Fisk had had long experience in nuclear weapons matters—in fact, Bell Labs had administered the Sandia nuclear weapons laboratory at Albuquerque—and seemed admirably qualified to head the team. He also happened to be an old friend of Bennie Schriever, who by now was about to pick up his fourth star as commander of the Air Force System Command. Bennie decided that I should brief Fisk and made a date for us to go to Bell Labs. He seemed almost certain that Fisk would be won over to the N-bomb, and that this, in turn, might have cause to impress upon high-ranking White House officials the importance of the concept. I warned him that he might be in for a disappointment. He told me I was dead wrong.

When we entered Fisk's office, it just so happened that he was in a long telephone conversation with one of those White House officials, McGeorge Bundy. Naturally they were discussing the test-ban negotiations. The conversation over, Fisk felt compelled to namedrop whom he had just spoken with and made a few remarks on how important his Geneva position was. I began to prepare myself for the worst. So did poor Bennie, who had expected the best.

A few minutes into the briefing it was obvious that Fisk couldn't have cared less. Bennie reached for a magazine and started reading, holding it directly in front of his face so that Fisk couldn't see how mad he was. I went through the motions, while Fisk paid essentially no attention. He made a few wisecracks now and then, while Bennie continued to "read" his magazine, still covering his face. Finally we were through. Bennie put down his magazine and asked Fisk what he thought about it. We received an arms control sermon. Fisk told us that the need to get a test ban superseded the need for any particular nuclear weapon, including the neutron bomb.

Bennie and I left and went downstairs to catch a cab, not saying a word to each other. What I felt like saying, I couldn't say: "I told you so." We got into the cab and drove away, still silent. And suddenly Bennie erupted with a string of expletives, the likes of which the cabbie had probably never heard.

* * *

As far as the Kennedy administration was concerned, the N-bomb was dead. As far as much of the rest of Washington was concerned, it had to stay alive as long as the moratorium was alive. By mid-1961 the N-bomb proponents (genuine and otherwise) and the moratorium opponents (who mainly professed to like the Bomb now) had marshaled their forces for a full-scale attack on the moratorium. Since members of the executive branch didn't dare open their mouths publicly for fear the White House would chop off their heads, the antimoratorium chorus came from Congress. As the *Washington Star*'s Earl Voss wrote on June 5, 1961:

> Fear that Russia may get the jump on the United States in the development of a new type of nuclear weapon—the neutron bomb—is a major element in increasing pressures on President Kennedy to order the resumption of nuclear testing by the United States.
>
> A behind-the-scenes debate, now going on here, is reminiscent of the one in the Truman administration before President Truman decided to go ahead with the development of the hydrogen bomb.
>
> Much of the pressure on Mr. Kennedy is being put by influential members of Congress, Democrats and Republicans, to end the thirty-two-month moratorium on nuclear weapons testing. Their position is backed by the military services.
>
> There is some doubt among President Kennedy's advisors, however, on how fundamentally important it would be to have the neutron bomb in the United States' arsenal . . .
>
> Advocates of full-speed development of the neutron bomb complain that President Kennedy has not been given the full facts on its military usefulness. He is said to have received reports only on scientific aspects of the weapon, not on the wide range of military applications reported possible . . .

My briefings to congressmen, most of which were initiated by Senator Dodd, increased substantially. And now, all of a sudden, it became possible to brief the former President and Vice-President who had remained so inaccessible while in office.

Early one morning in July 1961, while in Washington, I received a call from Admiral Radford. Richard Nixon was also in town, and was staying at the Statler. He had an hour open after breakfast and was willing to have me come and brief him. Would I come? I grabbed a cab, got down there well before the appointed time. Radford was waiting for me. We knocked on the door of Nixon's suite, were ushered in by Rosemary Woods and then proceeded to wait (I'd love to say for eighteen minutes, but it was a lot longer). Finally the great man entered. I thought I was watching an old Edward G. Robinson movie.

Nixon appeared wearing a very loud dressing robe and smoking a very long, very black cigar, which stayed in his mouth most of the time he spoke, which was most of the time. Radford made a few introductory remarks and then motioned for me to start the performance. I'd barely gotten started before Nixon interrupted, not to ask a question but to make a remark. This pattern continued through most of the next two hours, and I doubt whether I said 10 percent of what I'd intended to say. Nixon got very little of what I knew about the neutron bomb, but I sure got a lot of what he knew about the politics surrounding the Bomb. (His choice of language was similar to what he used around Haldeman and Erlichman; maybe I was being complimented.)

I wound up learning a helluva lot more than he did and I was tremendously impressed with him. He was unbelievably knowledgeable about nuclear politics, which seemed to be all that he cared to talk about that morning. Whereas he didn't go through the ceiling on the neutron bomb—how could he, he never found out about it—he did give me the impression that he thought the United States needed more effective and credible tactical nuclear capabilities. Being hopping mad at Kennedy, whom I'd voted for because he had seemed to be more realistic on defense than Nixon, at this juncture I told myself that I had voted for the wrong guy. If Nixon ran again, by God, he'd surely get my vote. He did, and look what happened.

That afternoon Radford called me again. As a result of our get-together, Nixon wanted to write an article on neutron bombs, tactical nuclear weapons and nuclear testing, to get out in the newspapers. Would I ghost one for him? I did it gladly.

At that time I had very little doubt that had Nixon won in 1960, he would have given a green light to the neutron bomb. I still believe that. If I'm right, then why didn't he move on the Bomb after he was elected in 1968? I don't profess to know the answer, but I'll make a guess: Henry Kissinger.

When Kissinger entered the White House in 1969, he made no effort to change the nuclear policies of the Kennedy-Johnson years, and did nothing of substance to address the issue of tactical nuclear weapons seriously. It is strange that the man who wrote the first truly definitive work on tactical nuclear weapons in a book that made him famous (*Nuclear Weapons and Foreign Policy,* which came out in 1957), chose to give little more than lip service to the subject when he came into power. It is tragic, I believe, that he didn't. Because at that time the Soviets were about to overtake us in tactical nuclear capabilities.

This they did while we stood still (as we also stood still, insofar as our strategic capabilities were concerned, while SALT I was being negotiated). As a consequence, they gained full superiority in ground force capabilities, a superiority that has been expanding continually. Short of a drastic overhauling of U.S. policy and no war in the meantime, there is no way of redressing this imbalance. Neutrons, schmeutrons, or any other public-relations gimmick the United States chooses to propagandize—we cannot solve the problem until we choose to recognize the problem. And we haven't done that since 1961. Kissinger recognized the problem a quarter-century ago. He ignored it during his eight years in Washington. Since leaving the government, he brings it up periodically and his logic is impeccable. Why doesn't he put his heart where his logic is?

A few weeks after getting together with Nixon, I received a call from Lewis Strauss. He wanted to have Jack Morse and me go to Gettysburg with him to tell Eisenhower about the neutron bomb. So we drove up.

Ike, wearing a very conservative business suit (with vest), cordially ushered us into his office (of very austere decor). Strauss gave him some background on the Bomb, and then came the briefing. Eisenhower was very attentive, hardly interrupted at all, and when he did, it was to ask questions, not give opinions.

Finally we were through. Strauss eagerly asked Ike what he thought about the concept. Well, he thought that it was a pretty interesting technical idea, but not very relevant. Should there ever be a situation where we had to use tactical nuclear weapons, it would coincide with the use of strategic nuclear weapons. The whole shooting match would be on, and the main thermonuclear stage would eclipse any little tactical stage and render meaningless such refinements as neutron weapons to be used in tactical warfare.

Strauss was crushed. Jack Morse got mad and began to argue with Ike. Among other things, he told Ike that he had been taken in by ideologically motivated scientists on the test moratorium. "Like whom?" said Ike. "Like Wiesner," [Jerome Wiesner, who was now Kennedy's science advisor] said Jack. Whereupon Ike allowed that he had been very impressed with Wiesner when he was a member of his Science Advisory Committee. Now Jack was crushed, too. We left quietly and drove back to Washington quietly. Unlike Bennie Schriever, Strauss did not choose to vent his ire via the expletive route. (Also a bit crushed was John Eisenhower, still his father's aide, who was working downstairs when we left his dad's office. He didn't seem too happy with his dad's reaction.) Eisenhower did just about as much for the N-bomb cause as Nixon: nothing.

By now the Russians were becoming concerned about the N-bomb and the U.S. test-moratorium position. The pressures on Kennedy to get back to nuclear testing were mounting by the day. So the Russians decided, as they always have when it looks like the United States might be getting serious about its nuclear arsenal, to start an antineutron-bomb propaganda campaign—very similar to the one they launched in 1977. One of the first blasts came from Nikita Khrushchev, during a speech given to the Rumanian Party Congress in Bucharest:

> More and more frequently now, we hear talk from statesmen and military leaders, particularly in the United States, that they are working toward the creation of a neutron bomb. The neutron bomb, according to the concept of its creators, should kill everything alive, but preserve material assets.
>
> Yes, comrades, so these people think. They are acting on the principle of robbers wanting to kill a man in such a way

> that his suit will not be stained with blood, in order to appropriate the suit. This, in effect, is what the neutron bomb is . . . to develop a bomb by means of which it would be possible to kill people but to preserve all riches—here it is, the bestial ethics of the most aggressive representatives of imperialism. Is this the law of man? Man to them is nothing. For them the main thing is to plunder, a quest for profit which prods the imperialists to the most horrible crimes.

Other Soviet spokesmen joined in, expressing variations on Khrushchev's theme of U.S. antihumanism:

> This is the morality of monsters. The plans for development of a neutron bomb expose all the inhuman essence of modern imperialism, no longer satisfied with merciless exploitation of working people and ready, for the sake of profit, to turn to crimes which, by their monstrosity, would eclipse the memory of the gas chambers and murder vans of the Hitlerite hangmen.

This assault continued up to and past (to the present moment) a day that shocked the United States and most of the civilized world. This was September 1, 1961, the day the Soviets announced they were ending the moratorium. And they did this with the most massive series of hydrogen bomb tests of all time.

Suddenly the N-bomb champions had nothing to say about the necessity to go back to testing. It was clear that Kennedy would have no other choice. It was also clear, in view of the circumstances, that the administration, despite its policies on N-bombs, would hardly dare to prevent their testing. Thanks to the priorities that had been established on N-bomb development, the Livermore lab had made considerable theoretical progress. The next year it was ready to begin testing. A series of tests were conducted underground in Nevada. They were highly successful.

By the spring of 1963 sufficient progress had been made to allow the testing of a device that could be "weaponized" to fit into a battlefield-delivery system: a bomb dropped from a tactical aircraft, a rocket such as the Honest John, already developed by the army, or a guided missile such as the Lance, whose development had just gotten underway. It was not small enough, however, for use in an artillery projectile. The test was made; it worked out extremely well.*

In fact, it was a far better neutron warhead than the one now being produced for the Lance missile. Which says a lot, quite a lot, about the direction we've been going on N-bomb development for almost the last twenty years, and how seriously the government has regarded the N-bomb's potential. At least in the case of the Lance neutron warhead, the direction has been *backward.*

With this success under its belt, Livermore, now under the direction of Johnny Foster, tried to get a customer for its product. Johnny fired off a letter to AEC Chairman Glen Seaborg, telling him of the lab's success and requesting that Seaborg ask the Pentagon to evaluate this proven neutron warhead for incorporation into a suitable delivery system. Seaborg sent Johnny's request over to Defense Secretary Robert McNamara, who decided to give the evaluation to the JCS first.

The JCS study (in which I participated) weighed favorably on the N-bomb and recommended that the Defense Department establish requirements for the successfully tested warhead. This was not what McNamara's office wanted to hear. The recommendation was ignored. Next it was decided to give the study to a Pentagon agency: the Office of Systems Analysis, then headed up by Alain Enthoven.

Enthoven, who had worked at RAND, where I knew him, had become McNamara's fair-haired boy on basic military policy. They both believed that complex military issues could best be addressed and resolved analytically, using refined mathematical procedures. However, at least on Enthoven's part, there was a strong ideological underpinning to his mathematics.

* The Livermore scientists in charge of the test invited me to come to the Nevada test site to "watch" it; namely, to see a small puff of dust arise from the desert floor, caused by the explosion a few hundred feet underground. I was to witness this event from the control center, where instruments would record, to small fractions of a millionth of a second, how the device behaved. This called for my security clearances to be on hand. When I arrived the day before the test, which was scheduled to take place early in the morning, my clearances had not arrived; they never did. As a result I slept late, had a good breakfast, turned around and headed home. I found out later how the shot had made out.

Enthoven had come from a school of thought at RAND that maintained there were no rational or meaningful nuclear solutions for fighting and winning ground wars. The thinking of this RAND group affected key advisors to Senator John F. Kennedy when he was mounting his campaign for the presidency. And the results of their ideological thinking on Kennedy were obvious long before he moved into the White House.

When McNamara came into the Pentagon, Enthoven became what was probably his closest and most influential advisor. The best way to present what Enthoven and his systems analysis colleagues in the Pentagon (several of whom also had come from RAND) thought about tactical nuclear weapons is to quote what he wrote after leaving the Pentagon in 1969: "One of the first major policy changes sought by the Kennedy administration in 1961 was to reduce the reliance on nuclear weapons for deterrence and defense, and increase the reliance on conventional forces, especially in NATO."

Before Enthoven had been assigned the task of evaluating the neutron warhead for possible use on the Lance missile, a mutual friend of ours had requested that he get my views on the matter. I went to his office (not too happily, I might say) and explained the situation to him. He listened intently and did not disagree with anything I said. I hadn't expected any disagreement and certainly hadn't expected to make a convert out of him. However, what I never expected was that he would countenance the most outrageous study I've ever come across.

It wasn't until the study was finished that I became aware of it. (When the Kennedy guys came in, my relationship with the Office of the Secretary of Defense dropped off to approximately zero. Those in key positions, like Enthoven, had no use for my views. Unless I went to the trouble of finding out what was going on, nobody was going to tell me.) So it happened that a friend of mine, who was working for Johnny Foster (who by now had moved into the Pentagon to replace Harold Brown as R&D chief), suggested that I go over the study for him. He called the army colonel who had been put in charge of the study, and told him I'd be over to see him.

I sat down with this Colonel C. and he went through his study, which had to do with what kind of warhead to put in the Lance battlefield missile. I plied him with questions about his basic assumptions (the results of all studies stem from the assumptions that are fed into them), and while he was explaining his calculations, I was doing mine. When he was finished, I informed him that his results were in error. Expecting that I was about to tell him that he was off by a factor of two, or something on that order, he modestly admitted to this possibility. (What the hell, we don't have that precise an understanding and you might be right in your assessment.) He could afford to be modest, since his results had found the neutron warhead at issue so ineffective compared with much higher-yield (bigger bang) fission weapons that being off by a factor of two would cause no worry.

But now I explained to him that the error was somewhat more than a factor of two. In fact, it seemed to be more like a factor of one hundred to one thousand, and I would be glad to prove it to him, if he wanted. This I did (hardly to his satisfaction). Whereupon he began to backtrack and put the blame on others who he claimed had fed him bum technical information. My response was that we all make errors (I was probably thinking of my thousandfold botch on the H-bomb radiation calculation), and that the study ought to be redone. His response was that it was too late for that. The Lance warhead already had been decided upon. It was to be a big dirty fission warhead, which he still thought was a better choice despite the errors in his study.

Now, I'd like to point out that the army was almost certainly aware of this study. (Hell, one of their own officers directed it.) The army had a lot of sharp guys in its nuclear requirements branch in the Pentagon, any one of whom could have seen how transparently phony these systems analysis calculations were. But did the army put up a fuss about the calculations? Hell, no! Why didn't it? Here's my reasoning: (1) The army was smart enough to know that pushing for the N-bomb would only put them in some degree of disfavor with their civilian masters; (2) Their civilian masters had made the army the most-favored military service (at least in dollar terms); and (3) The army had to get a warhead approved for the Lance missile, or they wouldn't be able to get approval for the missile, and the missile meant a helluva lot more to them than holding out for some nutty warhead that didn't destroy the buildings the army was used to destroying.

Upon leaving Colonel C., I made a beeline for the office of my friend who had arranged the meeting. I was in a rage. Surely a protest would be filed with McNamara, the decision would be overruled and a new study directed. My friend smiled and told me to take my outrage to his boss, Johnny Foster, who reported directly to McNamara. I went to see Johnny and explained what Colonel C. had done. He agreed that it was an atrocity. I demanded that Johnny expose this fraudulent study. He refused and explained: "You can't buck Alain Enthoven in this building. McNamara thinks the sun rises and sets with him and he just won't listen to me. It will be a waste of my time." Nobody was going to tackle Enthoven. The Lance decision held.

(As for the Colonel C. who had done this atrocious study, he received no punishment or rebuke. Instead, his career proceeded to blossom. When I next saw him, it was about ten years later, when the army had decided, after some jabbing by the Congress, to produce neutron warheads for its eight-inch artillery shell. I was asked to make a study showing how these weapons could reduce civilian damage (which they could, very substantially). After my study was completed, I traveled to the Pentagon to tell the army people about my findings. The senior officer there was, of all people, the former Colonel C. Only now he was a major general. He thought the N-bomb was great, the briefing was great, and boy, did he appreciate what I'd done. I felt ill.)

Not too many months after the Soviets broke the test moratorium, America's anger over this outrage had lowered to a degree where serious negotiations to end all nuclear testing commenced. By 1963 it appeared that there was more than a fair chance that the Russians would agree to inspection terms for a comprehensive test ban (i.e., total—banning of all tests) that would be acceptable to the United States. A treaty seemed perilously close. Those who were opposed to such a ban again went into high gear fighting it, about the same way they fought the moratorium. But now the game was different.

The end product was not to get the President to change his mind about a treaty. There was no way this could be done. He was hell-bent on a treaty, and nothing could change his mind on the need for one, unless of course, he became convinced that the Senate would not ratify one. Thus, the battle over men's minds now shifted to influencing senators. For unless two thirds of them voted to ratify a treaty, the treaty would be dead. Most active in this direction was Senator Dodd, who continued to emphasize the neutron bomb as the prime reason for not signing a treaty.

By now Dodd realized that there was no way that Kennedy was going to assign even a smidgen of importance to the Bomb. And like Eisenhower, Kennedy had refused to be drawn into open debate on the Bomb and its relevance to nuclear weapons testing. So Dodd decided to attack the administration, but did not strike directly at the President. Instead, he picked on the "sacred cows" surrounding Kennedy (many of whom had surrounded Eisenhower)—his scientific advisors.

On February 21, 1963, on the Senate floor, Dodd delivered an assault on the administration's nuclear policies and its position on the test ban. He specifically brought up the N-bomb:

> . . . I believe that I was the first member of the Congress to publicly discuss the possibilities of a neutron bomb. I did so as part of a detailed analysis of the entire test-ban situation . . .
>
> . . . the Joint Chiefs of Staff have recommended that the development of the neutron bomb be pursued on a high-priority basis, and the Congressional Joint Committee on Atomic Energy has been so impressed by the project that they have urged the President to support it . . .
>
> Our ignorance of Soviet progress in this field is, and will remain, complete; we shall know only what they choose to tell us. Such experiments are far too low in yield to be detected . . . Should they ever announce that they possess a neutron bomb, I pray that we shall be able, without delay, to announce a comparable capability.
>
> . . . I find it worrisome to an extreme to know that they may now possess, or will soon possess, the very weapon which could assist them immeasurably toward realizing their goals, for this weapon would permit them to achieve the coveted prize of Western Europe with an intact urban-industrial fabric, instead of battering it to rubble with atomic or hydrogen bombs, or even with high explosives as was the case in World War II.

Then Dodd launched into Kennedy's advisors:

> Despite the manifest advantages which the neutron bomb would have over existing tactical nuclear weapons, and de-

> spite the evidence that the Soviets have long ago initiated research in this field, the development of the neutron bomb has been pooh-poohed or minimized or discouraged by some of the President's scientific advisors and by other members of the administration.

Now, to keep the record straight, I have to point out that the neutron bomb Dodd was referring to here was of the so-called "pure-fusion" variety, one of the two concepts first exposed to me at Livermore in 1958. As I've explained earlier, this concept does not have a fission trigger to generate the fusion reactions. At the time of Dodd's remarks, the United States had not been successful in developing a pure-fusion neutron weapon. What *had* been successfully tested by Livermore was a fission-fusion neutron warhead that employed a fission explosive trigger. As will be discussed later (in Chapter 5) the pure-fusion variety represents the ultimate battlefield nuclear weapon in terms of flexibility of use.

Whereas the Eisenhower administration did not react to the very similar charges that Dodd had made three years earlier, this time around, the Kennedy people decided to do battle, using Adrian Fisher, the deputy director of the Arms Control and Disarmament Agency, as a spokesman. Via a series of "communications" fired back and forth between Dodd and Fisher, using *The Washington Post* as a go-between, a major debate ensued. It came to a sudden end when Fisher, writing directly to Dodd, violated the secrecy Dodd had complained about, by revealing the results of the Nevada N-bomb test series:

> With respect to the pure-fusion bomb, it should be pointed out that the development of such a weapon is by no means certain. Moreover, as you know, we have already made significant advances in the direction of tactical weapons with a smaller fission as compared with fusion component. There is, therefore, a real question as to the utility of a pure-fusion bomb over weapons already available . . .

Poor Fisher, whose letter to Dodd had been approved by several high administration officials, including key Kennedy advisors Jerome Wiesner and McGeorge Bundy, was suddenly in a jam. Some of the JCAE members were demanding his scalp for releasing allegedly "top secret" information. Fisher, who had come to know Dodd when they served as lawyers during the Nuremberg trials, came to Dodd's office asking for help in getting off the security hook. Dodd obligingly went to bat for him. Fisher was able to extricate himself from the mess. But he now had little gumption to go on with the debate. Dodd did reply to Fisher's ill-advised letter, going into a detailed defense of pure-fusion neutron bombs. However, that was the end of the debate.

As to who won or lost in the Dodd-Fisher tangle, like all debates on such controversial issues, this has to be a subjective judgment. However, "winning" the debate was not Dodd's primary purpose. He was out to get more senators on his side. In this he did rather well, receiving a number of very complimentary letters from his colleagues.

But now Senator Dodd was in a mess of his own. He was a loyal Democrat who had made himself very unpopular with a Democratic administration. He was at odds with a number of key Democrats in the Senate, including Hubert Humphrey, who were far from happy over his opposition to the Comprehensive Test Ban. It was becoming obvious that Kennedy could not get the Senate to go along with a Comprehensive Test Ban, but it was also obvious that he wanted some kind of a treaty. Next year Kennedy would be up for reelection. So would Dodd, who was beginning to sense that his opposition to the Comprehensive Test Ban was hurting him politically in his home state.

One day Dodd went to see Humphrey with a stunning proposal. Would he be willing to cosponsor a Senate resolution to offer the Russians an agreement to ban all nuclear tests in the atmosphere and underwater? What could Humphrey do, besides eat his heart out? He had been deftly preempted by just about the last guy in the Senate who would think up a ploy like this. He became cosponsor of the Dodd-Humphrey Resolution, which quickly picked up thirty-two other senators.

Kennedy now had senatorial support, which became overwhelming, for a treaty he could propose to the Russians, which he did and which the Russians accepted—to include banning tests in space as well as in the air and underwater. He also had an honest-to-gosh nuclear arms control treaty under his belt that he could parade before the voters the next year. And Dodd could now parade his laurels as a prince of peace to his constituents. (He won overwhelmingly the next year.)

After Senator Dodd had scored his great coup leading to the Partial Test Ban Treaty, I went to see him. I didn't think the treaty was a good idea. I wanted him to know it. He didn't disagree. In fact, later on he raised some of the most serious questions about it when it came up for Senate review; although he voted for it, of course. Almost affectionately, he told me: "Sam, a politician's first responsibility is to get elected." I still don't want to believe it.

All's well that ends well. Once the so-called Partial Test Ban Treaty was signed that summer, Kennedy pulled away from urgently seeking a comprehensive treaty. Meanwhile, Dodd and the other neutron bomb fans had no further reason to use the Bomb to fight such a treaty, and the administration had apparently succeeded in sacking the Bomb for good. The AEC activities on neutron bombs were put on the back burner, as it became obvious that requirements were not about to be established. Needless to say, this also represented to me the end of my neutron bomb crusade. My last briefing had been given. I was never again solicited for my advice. Nor was I consulted about what to do about N-bombs—even when the Pentagon was getting ready to propose them to the Congress ten years later, or any time after that.

CHAPTER 4
LIMBO AND REVIVAL

THE SONG HAD ENDED, BUT the melody lingered on. It had been an exciting, and eye-opening, five years for me. Washington had managed to get discriminate tactical nuclear weapons out of its system.* (From the time it dumped the N-bomb until Reagan

* A discriminate tactical nuclear weapon is one whose effects can be confined mainly to the military target, minimizing damage to non-combatants and their property. So neutron bombs, which are intended to kill enemy sol-

made his N-bomb production decision in August 1981, not *one* new warhead reflecting advanced discriminate technology entered the U.S. arsenal.) But I had not gotten them out of my system.

However, going back to RAND and continuing my discriminate ways was not easy. By this time the Pentagon, including the military, had fully accepted the McNamara (better yet, Enthoven) doctrine. Think tanks were hardly encouraged to work in this area. RAND got the message and, like practically everyone else, cut down drastically its work on tactical nuclear weapons. Not me, however, and I stubbornly continued my pursuits. My guess is that I would have been rewarded for my stubbornness by being fired, had it not been for Bennie Schriever.

At this point Bennie was in bad trouble with the Pentagon, giving one a rough idea of the loyalty of the "System" to accomplished, dedicated military men. Bennie had not only masterminded the first ICBM development and worked miracles by taking it from the drawing board to an operational capability in only a few years, he had also set the stage for the U.S. entry into space. But the old punchline goes: "What have you done for me lately?" And what Bennie had done was to fight McNamara's policies tooth and nail. His reward was that he was denied any opportunity for advancement and left alone to run his fiefdom—the Air Force Systems Command. Had he not had powerful support in the Congress and in the aerospace industry, McNamara might have succeeded in forcing him out.

So Bennie remained in uniform. He also let RAND know that he was desirous of my services, and since he was still a force to be reckoned with, RAND complied and I wound up doing most of my work as an advisor to General Schriever. He let me form small committees to evaluate some of my new ideas and was willing to take responsibility for my nuclear escapades. I'll get around to describing some of these notions—the majority of them involving nuclear radiation—later. But let me tell you a little story relating to how acceptable these notions were in Washington.

---

diers but spare civilians and their towns, are, by this definition, discriminate weapons. For example, had they been available in the Korean War for use against enemy soldiers fighting in the city of Seoul, their application would have represented a highly discriminate attack—far more so than was the attack that actually took place using conventional weapons, and which pretty well leveled the city.

In 1965 I was invited to speak on discriminate tactical nuclear weapons before a number of key policy planners in the U.S. Department of State. I've never been able to figure out why, unless these planners were interested in sizing up the enemy; i.e., me, not the Russians. I described to them a number of these discriminate possibilities—including neutron bombs.

It soon became evident that virtually all those present, however intrigued they may have been from a technical point of view, were adamantly opposed to the development and use of such weapons from a political viewpoint. These prospects, they maintained, held no potential political utility. However, I steadfastly continued with my discourse on discrimination.

At one point, in introducing the next weapon concept, I announced: "I am going to describe a tactical nuclear weapon concept that gives only conventional weapon effects on the target." Specifically this concept involved the notion of using a nuclear explosive to propel chunks of metal at extremely high velocities. Upon impacting on the target, the chunks would penetrate some distance, then vaporize and blow up, causing the same effects as would buried high-explosive charges. Were such a weapon feasible, not only would this technique—backed up by the power of the Atom—be far more effective than high explosive attacks, but it could provide an even greater degree of discriminate application than large high-explosive bombs toward destroying military targets.

Having brought out the features of a nuclear weapon that acts against the target like a conventional weapon, I expected that there might be a break in the ranks of this antinuclear audience. No such thing happened. The opposition remained unanimous, for the simple reason that it was not really the nature of the effects that counted. Rather, it was the fact that a nuclear explosion was taking place over the area of theater operations. As Gertrude Stein might have said it: "A nuke is a nuke is a nuke . . ."

Now beginning to wonder how deep the feelings of this group might be on the issue of nuclear weapons, I tried a different tack. In principle, I explained, one could devise a giant nuclear explosive cannon where very low-yield explosives could shoot massive conventional weapon payloads over many hundreds of miles. The military weapons effects—purely conventional—would be felt only in the theater, the source of energy required to deliver these weapons would be well outside the theater zone. "Would this scheme be acceptable?" I asked. And the answer again, and unanimously, was "No!" "Not even if the nuclear explosions took place in the United States?" I wondered. "Not even in the United States" was the adamant response.

Clearly, at this point the depth of official feeling against the military use of nuclear explosives had been pretty well communicated to me. By now I realized that as long as a nuclear explosive was used in anger, U.S. policy held the type of explosive and geographical location of detonation to be absolutely irrelevant. The cardinal point was that it was the act of detonating the explosive in anger that was a political taboo.

By now what little innocence I had left on nuclear-explosive policy matters had been completely spoiled. But my intellectual curiosity had become boundless over the broader issue of nuclear energy for military purposes. So I wondered openly before the planners about alternate possibilities and proceeded down a similar path, this time propelling high-explosive payloads with nonexplosive nuclear-propulsion devices. I pointed out that at that time, the United States was actively developing a powerful nuclear rocket engine that could allegedly put large payloads into deep space more efficiently than normal chemical-fueled engines could. Would it run against the grain of policy if these nuclear-reactor-powered rockets, fired from the U.S., were to propel massive high-explosive payloads into a theater of hostilities halfway around the world?

With this nonexplosive nuclear query, a first breach in the dike appeared. A small minority in the group held that this might not conflict with the ongoing U.S. policy. But the rest were not to be swayed, and it appeared certain that were such a weapon system to be seriously proposed by the U.S. military, the policy makers in State would turn thumbs down. At the same time, however—and by now I had begun to view my audience with no small degree of incredulity—I suddenly realized that a moment of worldly reality in the discussion was at hand. There was another nuclear reactor scheme for launching conventional payloads over considerable distances that was actually in the U.S. arsenal—namely, the nuclear-powered aircraft carrier.

So now came the final question on using nuclear energy for military purposes. It was a weapons system actually in hand, the

U.S.S. *Enterprise,* and an actual ongoing war, in Southeast Asia. How did the group feel about the policy aspects of sending the *Enterprise* into the waters of the South China Sea, to launch jet aircraft loaded with high-explosive bombs to attack targets in the theater?

Suddenly a real split in the group developed, and whereas the consensus still weighed against the Atom, it was by no means overwhelmingly so. Some months later a policy decision was made by the United States to dispatch the *Enterprise* to the Vietnam theater. There it stayed, to launch many thousands of fighter-bomber sorties from the deck. (As to how other nations regard the military use of nuclear energy in a shooting war, look at what happened last year in the Falkland Islands. The British, who have been rabidly antinuclear compared to us, wasted no time in dispatching two nuclear-powered attack submarines, one of which promptly sunk the Argentine cruiser *Belgrano* outside the British-prescribed off-limits zone. I doubt whether the thought of checking this out with us ever entered their minds.)

Around the time of my talk at State, the mid-1960's, we were getting mired up to our ears in Vietnam. Whereas anyone in the Pentagon who was caught thinking seriously of using nuclear weapons in this conflict would find his neck in the wringer in short order,* this did not keep Bennie or me from thinking about it. Since the biggest military problem in those days, which was in fact the biggest problem of the war, happened to be the guerrilla forces, I put my mind to work on how nuclear weapons might be used to thwart the Vietcong.

To gain a more realistic knowledge of what was going on in Vietnam, I went to Hawaii, where a longtime friend of mine was Commander of the Pacific Air Forces. This was General Hunter Harris, who was one of the first nuclear strategic thinkers in the

* In March 1967 the Defense Department issued a news release saying:

> There is no military requirement for the use of nuclear weapons or devices in the current situation in Vietnam. The Joint Chiefs of Staff have no proposal under consideration for the use of nuclear weapons or devices in Vietnam and they have made no proposal to the Secretary of Defense for the use of nuclear weapons or devices in Vietnam. Nor is any other responsible official of the Department of Defense considering the use of any nuclear weapon or device in Vietnam.

air force after World War II, and who had taught an indoctrination course in nuclear strategy I attended. Hunter, who had known Bennie from the Army Air Corps days of the 1930's, was most obliging in putting his staff at my disposal to provide me with background information.

I began to get ideas, which I would report to Bennie and to Hunter Harris. All of them involved radiation, and almost all of them were based on applying neutron warheads, one way or another. Bennie decided that I ought to get a little closer to the war, so he sent me off to Vietnam on an orientation trip with a group of his officers. My orders were not to tell anybody what was in the back of my mind. This succeeded in firming up my opinions even more.

On a subsequent visit to Hawaii General Harris made a courageous decision. He would have his command formulate military requirements for some of the weapons concepts I had told him about. He asked me to work with his nuclear weapons planners, which I was more than delighted to do. A requirements paper was shaped up, coordinated with the other military commands and sent to CINCPAC (Commander-in-Chief Pacific). CINCPAC put an okay on it and shipped it off to the Joint Chiefs in the Pentagon. There it came to an end. I guess the Chiefs wanted to stay Chiefs.

In 1966 Schriever decided that he wasn't going to sweat out the full time allowed to him to stay in uniform. He retired early. And there went my guardian angel. I was now stuck at RAND wondering what to do with myself. So I did a stupid thing, I decided to write up all of my collective thoughts on using nuclear weapons in Vietnam and put them out in the form of a RAND report, to be read by people back in Washington and other places.

I finished a draft of the report and turned it over to the reports editor in my department for his gussying up. The next thing I knew, my department head came into my office, closed the door and pleaded with me to drop the whole crazy idea. Not only did he fear the report getting out of RAND, he even feared it getting *into* RAND. For his sake, and for my sake, would I not only drop the idea of the report, but would I drop my work on tactical nuclear weapons and turn to nonnuclear weapons ideas on fighting the war in Vietnam? I got the message and said okay, I'd do that. The alternative was to look for another job and there wasn't one to be had.

One of the ideas I had involved detonating large charges of high-intensity flash powder, like a quarter-pound's worth, to flash-blind the Vietcong who were going down jungle trails or approaching South Vietnamese villages at night. My calculations had convinced me that this could immobilize the VC for a respectable fraction of an hour, during which time the defending forces could home in on the flash, which could be seen a long way off, and probably be able to capture the VC while they were still rubbing their eyes. I tried to get the military interested, to no avail. So I decided to put out the notion in an article for some military journal. To do this, I first had to submit the article to the Pentagon for clearance. I was denied the right to get it published on the grounds that high-intensity flash powder was an inhumane weapon.

You can imagine my feeling a couple of years ago when I read about the British using exactly this technique to paralyze momentarily some terrorists who had taken over an embassy in London. It worked beautifully. Needless to say, it did no lasting physical harm to either the terrorists or their captives. Considering what might have happened if the embassy had been stormed by force, I'd say that this was a pretty humane idea. I'd also say that the offhand rejection of off-the-beaten-path notions such as this symbolized the U.S. inability to come to grips with the realities of the Vietnam War.

I had still another idea, a nuclear idea, again involving light, which I knew from the start would be rejected, but which I was allowed to work on because it didn't involve nuclear *weapons*. This one involved taking small amounts of radioactive material (produced by absorbing neutrons, incidentally), mixing them with a substance that would become luminescent when bombarded by the electrons (known as beta rays) emitted by the material. (I decided to dub this concept "Watch Dial," since it was based on exactly the same principle as the radium watch dials of yesteryear which would permit you to tell time at night.) The luminescent mixture would be imbedded into transparent plastic strips, and one side of the strip coated with a light-reflecting substance. The strips would then be rolled up and shipped off to the country whose villages were being terrorized by guerrillas at night.

The strips could be taped to the upper branches of trees outside the threatened villages, illuminating the area below with the same basic purpose in mind as emplacing sodium-vapor streetlights in a high-crime area. Hopefully the guerrillas, fearing that they would be seen as they approached the village, would turn back. If they didn't, the defenders, hiding in the dark, would have a big advantage.

The strips could also be enmeshed in fencing around the villages in essentially the same manner that lighting is installed around protective fencing guarding key installations. The defenders would again have the advantage of being able to see the guerrillas without the guerrillas seeing them.

The cost of doing this turned out to be very reasonable. There were no radiological hazards because of the small amounts of radioactivity involved, and because of the nature of the radiation emitted. The idea seemed to be a lot more reliable than using electric lighting, where the lights and the electric generators could be shot up by the guerrillas. However, as I said, there was no conceivable way to stir up interest in this notion, for one very simple reason: It was *nuclear.*

Although by now I pretty well understood the intensity of antinuclear feeling by the U.S. government affecting the prosecution of the Vietnam War, I still found myself wondering why it was okay to use harmless amounts of radioactivity to tell the time, but it was not okay to try to help save the lives of women and children who were being murdered by the Vietcong.

The issue of the neutron bomb did not die, however. I watched from the sidelines, and I recalled how during the early 1960's, when Senator Dodd was parading me around to talk to his colleagues, one of those I briefed was Senator Stuart Symington (D-Missouri). The senator looked kindly on the concept, requested reports on the subject and asked me to drop in any time he wasn't busy so we could continue discussing the subject. He genuinely wanted to help. By this time, however, prospects for the N-bomb had dropped to zero because of the Kennedy administration policies. Symington, being a practical politician and realizing that there was nothing he could do, did essentially nothing. But apparently he did not forget.

Now, in the early 1970's, the Atomic Energy Commission, in accordance with requirements coming from the Pentagon, completed developments on two new nuclear warheads for the army's 155-millimeter and 8-inch artillery shells. The existing warheads were getting on in years. They were products of the 1950's, and had to be replaced. However, the replacements employed the same warhead technology as the old shells, namely a technology based on nuclear fission. For the reasons brought out previously, there wasn't the slightest official interest by the army in neutron warheads. Even had there been such interest, it would have been politically impossible to establish requirements.

Expecting no real difficulties, the Pentagon and the AEC sought production funding for these two shells. However, their expectations failed to materialize when the JCAE Subcommittee on Military Applications, chaired by Senator Symington, held hearings on the proposed U.S. nuclear weapons stockpile. The congressmen were clearly unimpressed with the proposed new artillery warheads. They opposed their production. They were upset by the excessive cost of the warheads and by the fact that they represented technological stagnation. One of the most powerful committee members, Representative Chet Holifield, who had formerly chaired the JCAE, questioned the Pentagon's wisdom and favored canceling the whole business:

> Why do we persist in this type of obsolete weapon? . . . I have never been able to understand the reasoning of how you take such an expensive weapon with such limited mobility and with such contaminating qualities to it . . . I think it ought to be abolished, the whole system.

Then, in the course of the hearings, Symington got to the point, asking a series of questions designed to show his own preference for neutron warheads and to put the Pentagon on the spot by demanding an explanation of why such warheads had been turned down in the past.

The hearings over, the JCAE shocked the army by turning thumbs down on the artillery warheads. This, in turn, left the army with a dilemma: It had to have new warheads, the existing ones having severe operational limitations. But it really didn't care very much for neutron warheads with this mysterious radiation stuff. They wanted a weapon that would knock an enemy tank off its treads and all that tangible stuff. And they really weren't very much more concerned about civilian collateral damage than they had been twenty years ago.

However, the resolution of the dilemma really wasn't difficult. It was much more important to have a reliable weapon that could go bang in time to be of some good than to put up a fuss over what was in the bang. As a result, and almost certainly influenced by Symington's druthers (after all, he happened to be *the* key guy in Congress on nuclear weapons), the army was persuaded, or persuaded itself, or both (now everyone who was in on the act wants to take credit), to take a look at neutrons.

Shortly after the Congress turned thumbs down, the Secretary of Defense (James Schlesinger) issued a directive to the army to go back to the drawing board and come up with new proposals. This in turn resulted in the Army's Chief of Staff initiating a study to "reexamine" nuclear warhead requirements for artillery projectiles.

The Chief's memo (dated August 29, 1973) requesting the study is full of radiation-dose requirements for incapacitating military personnel, with the concomitant requirement to "minimize collateral damage," i.e., damage to the civilian structure. In other words, the memo directed a neutron bomb study. It also happened to be unclassified, and had a cagey reporter assigned to the Pentagon gotten his hands on this memo, he could have reached the inevitable conclusion and picked a real scoop almost four years before a *Washington Post* reporter "exposed" congressional testimony indicating that a neutron warhead would be produced for the Lance missile. Or, one year before the *Post* revelation, any reporter who bothered to read the news bulletin of the U.S. Energy Agency would have noted that a senior agency official had said that the eight-inch artillery shell nuclear warhead under development "will be the first U.S. weapon specially designed to reduce collateral damage from blast and radioactivity." Again, this could only be a neutron warhead.

When *The Washington Post* article came out on June 4, 1977, it was obvious there was a plot afoot to kill off the project before it could gain final congressional approval. A few days later the *Post* lead editorial, entitled "A New Warhead We Don't Need," lashed out at the N-bomb as being in the same camp with chemical and biological weapons, and as being a catalyst to general nuclear war. Suddenly the debate was on, but not in the form it had taken almost twenty years before. This time the chips were down, the debate was not over the necessity to develop neutron bombs, for that was a fait accompli. In the interim between the Army Chief of Staff's memo and the *Post* article, they had been developed. The argument now was over whether they should be built.

A few days after the *Post* editorial Congress got into the act. Key congressmen began an assault on the Bomb. One of them was Senator Mark Hatfield (R-Ore.), who referred to the neutron bomb as being "in the realm of the unconscionable." He offered an amendment to delete funding for the Lance neutron warhead. Hatfield said that he had been told by an unidentified nuclear scientist that the use of neutron bombs would spawn "a gaseous cloud of carbon-fourteen." The cloud, averred Hatfield, "would be carried into the upper atmosphere and would be deposited as fallout and have a half-life of six thousand years." This, claimed the senator, would be lethal to human beings. When I read this, I blew my top. (It was just about as accurate a scientific statement as that made by Senator Estes Kefauver in 1956, when he was campaigning with Adlai Stevenson. Continued hydrogen bomb tests, said Kefauver, would knock the earth sixteen degrees off its axis.)

Roughly speaking, for neutron bombs to produce the same level of carbon-14 (which is produced by nitrogen nuclei absorbing neutrons) that was generated by atmospheric testing prior to the Atmospheric Test Ban in 1963, something on the order of a *million* neutron blasts would have to occur. But even if this astronomical number of N-bombs were exploded, based on our knowledge of the results of the U.S. and Soviet hydrogen bomb tests leading up to 1963, no demonstrable, significant radiation damage to human beings would occur from carbon-14.

But explode a million neutron bombs. Holy cow! That would entail producing as much as one thousand times the number of bombs we expect to produce. Keep in mind that even with the current production order, our government tells us that this will allow us to hold back forty thousand Soviet tanks. So where does this "unidentified scientist" get off telling the senator about this

Copyright © 1977 by Herblock in The Washington Post

invidious radiation risk? No wonder he chose to be unidentified. So here we go again with scientists making gross misrepresentations of scientific fact when they're driven by an ideological bee in their bonnet.

Destiny, destiny! Senator Hatfield's amendment barely flunked the course, on a ten-to-ten tie, in the Senate Appropriations Committee. The Bomb lived. And began to prosper as other congressional committees took up the weapon, waxing more and more favorable. So did Jimmy Carter, who had originally been extremely cautious about taking a position. On July 11 Carter responded to a letter of inquiry from Senator John Stennis urging that the Congress approve the budgetary allocation for the Bomb. Carter also sought support for the Bomb in other countries. However, it was not readily forthcoming.

On July 9, 1977, TASS, the official Soviet news agency, challenged Jimmy Carter directly: "How can one pose as a champion of human rights and at the same time brandish the neutron bomb that threatens the lives of millions of people? Washington is trying hard to do both."

The Carter administration's "propaganda campaign about its 'love of man' is nothing more than rhetoric around a myth," the TASS commentary continued. "But its neutron bombs—just as the other new types of inhuman weapons of mass annihilation that are being launched into production—are a real fact. And facts, as is known, are a stubborn thing."

In West Germany, Egon Bahr, general secretary of the Social Democratic Party, declared the neutron bomb to be "a symbol for the perversion of human thinking." Its development proved that "mankind is about to go mad," said Bahr, who also noted: "It seems to be an ideal of latest progress that it is easier to clear away human bodies than to remove the rubble of cities and factories." Furthermore, the West German defense minister rebuked the then NATO military commander, General Alexander Haig, who claimed at that time that Germany had given "enthusiastic support" to the N-bomb. The minister said: "It is not true that we Germans have shown special interest within NATO for the neutron bomb."

Forty-two East German intellectuals, including physicist Klaus Fuchs, who more than thirty years earlier had given the Russians U.S. atomic bomb secrets, condemned the neutron bomb as an abominable example of the misuse of science.*

* Fuchs was in my section, the Theoretical Division, at Los Alamos during the war. I'll never forget a talk he gave describing the performance of a high-explosive component of the bomb that destroyed Nagasaki. At talk's end, Oppenheimer, who was in the audience, heaped the highest praise on Fuchs, stating that this was as fine work as he had seen so far at Los Alamos. Undoubtedly it was.

"THERE ARE STRONG MORAL OBJECTIONS TO A BOMB THAT KILLS BUT DOESN'T DESTROY BUILDINGS. FIX IT SO IT DESTROYS BUILDINGS, TOO."

DUNAGIN'S PEOPLE by Ralph Dunagin © 1977 Field Enterprises, Inc.
Courtesy of Field Newspaper Syndicate

In Japan, on August 9, the date of the first atomic bombing, memorial rites for the Hiroshima victims were observed. A featured speaker, United Nation's General Assembly President H. Shirley Amerasinghe, used the occasion to denounce the N-bomb: "Scientists must realize that although their achievements are dazzling in their brilliance, their products are satanic. The most recent obscenity is the neutron bomb, a weapon which will destroy human life, but spare human property."

With all this static, Carter began to back away from the Bomb. The deployment decision he was supposed to make was post-

"It's simple! There aren't any people around the castle, because of the neutron bomb!"

poned. And in effect, he put the kiss of death on the Bomb by announcing that he would attempt to develop a consensus among NATO European officials on deployment. There would be a "continuing series of meetings until a consensus is conveyed to us," and these meetings would continue "until the end of the year." The meetings continued well past the end of the year.

In the United States in the meantime, the neutron bomb had become as popular as apple pie. In September the House voted down an amendment to kill budgetary authorization by about

3–1. The Senate had already approved funding by a 3–2 vote. The majority of the press had come out in favor of production.

In Europe, however, resistance was still mounting, and U.S. efforts to push the N-bomb began to run into increasing difficulties. An October meeting of NATO's Nuclear Planning Group (NPG) to discuss the Bomb's fate ended with a decision still up in the air. This only succeeded in making the Carter administration push even harder to make the weapons more palatable. The U.S. hard-sell was taking on a distinct scent of hucksterism.

At the NPG meeting a U.S. official told the press: "It's not our purpose to jam anything down anyone's throat. If it's not desired, it won't be produced. Outside the alliance, it had no utility." Defense Secretary Harold Brown was interviewed during the meeting, where he stated that the neutron bomb "is intended as a deterrent against a massive attack from the Warsaw Pact, and if none ever comes, then this weapon would never be used."*

The hassle went on, and on. European governments continued to balk, and began to suggest that the neutron bomb dilemma be resolved at the arms control conference table. The United States made an effort to use the Bomb as a "bargaining chip" in negotiations with the Russians, but quickly found out that you can't bargain with what you don't have. The Russians pointed out this illogic and repeated their insistence that the neutron bomb be banned, not negotiated. The day before Christmas, Leonid Brezhnev delivered a nasty yuletide greeting to NATO European governments—either join into an agreement to ban the Bomb or the USSR would be forced to develop it. "The Soviet Union is resolutely opposed to the development of the neutron bomb . . ." said Brezhnev, "but if such a bomb were developed in the West, developed against us—a fact which nobody even tries to conceal—the latter must clearly recognize that the USSR will not remain a passive onlooker . . ." As the year came to an end, the mess was as messy as ever. As the next year unfolded, the mess remained unchanged.

* The Carter administration either forgot (which must have been the case with Harold Brown, who knew better) or never knew that the neutron bomb was not developed with European application in mind.

In March of 1978, at the thirty-nation disarmament conference in Geneva, the Soviet delegate proposed a treaty to prohibit the production, stockpiling and deployment of the neutron bomb, while denouncing the weapon as "cruel and barbaric." It then fell upon the U.S. delegate to defend the weapon. The delegate was, of all people, Adrian Fisher, Kennedy's front man for doing a public hatchet job on the Bomb in 1963. While Fisher relayed the Carter administration party line to the conference, in private he told the U.S. delegation: "I don't want my epitaph to say I defended the neutron bomb."

In Europe around this time, the Dutch in particular were really putting up a fuss. The Dutch premier tried to soften the opposition by linking the deployment decision to the talks with the Russians to ban deployment. This was not negative enough for his defense minister, who resigned in protest. Nor was it satisfactory to the Parliament, which adopted a resolution opposing deployment on Dutch soil. After that, forty thousand people marched in the rain through Amsterdam protesting the weapon as inhuman.

By now the Carter administration had become discouraged. It abruptly changed course in its dialogue with the Europeans and canceled a scheduled meeting at which the U.S. had been hoping, finally, to gain allied support. Something was going on in Washington. It was conjectured (I think correctly) that Carter had decided to defer the issue for a while so that he could get on with other matters with the Soviets. (Like SALT II, which was getting nowhere, among other reasons because of the neutron bomb fracas. The Soviets, including Brezhnev, had been screaming to practically everyone willing, or unwilling, to listen, that so long as the United States pressed for the fiendish neutron weapon, productive strategic arms control talks were out of the question.) A few days later it became obvious what had been going on. The President ruled against producing the Bomb. And all hell broke out.

Suddenly, except for the Soviets and Soviet-influenced countries, just about everyone was mad at the President. If they had been for the Bomb, they felt betrayed. If they had been against it, they felt that Carter could have killed it more gracefully than he did. Even *The Washington Post,* which had tried so hard to do in the Bomb, allowed that Soviet actions had "made it more, not less, desirable for [Carter] to let the weapons go forward at least to the procurement stage." Like most European countries, they felt that Carter's decision had made fools of them.

Plainly the President had overdone it. Enormous pressures for him to reverse his decision began to mount. Just a few days later he had another change of mind. This time he decided to defer on actual production, but ordered the development of the so-called neutron "component," a receptacle containing heavy hydrogen, which could be added to a fission warhead to turn it into an honest-to-gosh neutron weapon. In more pragmatic terms, since the bottom line on neutron bombs had to be their incorporation into the NATO stockpile, he decided not to decide to decide. In other words, he decided not to decide on their production, which in turn put off even further the decision to deploy them to Europe. Here is how he expressed it:

> I have decided to defer production of weapons with enhanced radiation effects. The ultimate decision regarding the incorporation of enhanced radiation features into our modernized battlefield weapons will be made later, and will be influenced by the degree to which the Soviet Union shows restraint in its conventional and nuclear arms programs and force deployments affecting the security of the United States and Western Europe.
>
> Accordingly, I have ordered the Defense Department to proceed with the modernization of the Lance missile nuclear warhead and the eight-inch (artillery) weapon system, leaving open the option of installing the enhanced radiation elements.
>
> The United States is consulting with its partners in the North Atlantic alliance on this decision and will continue to discuss with them appropriate arms-control measures to be pursued with the Soviet Union.
>
> We will continue to move ahead with our allies to modernize and strengthen our military capabilities, both conventional and nuclear. We are determined to do whatever is necessary to assure our collective security and the forward defense of Europe.

It was now obvious that Carter didn't want to build the Bomb.* As for his warning to the Soviets that his ultimate decision on the neutron bomb "will be influenced by the degree to which the Soviet Union shows restraint in its conventional and nuclear arms programs and force deployments . . .", this turned out to be little more than bluster. The Soviets went ahead and methodically improved and increased their capabilities, including the development of the vaunted SS-20 intermediate-range ballistic missile (which probably has the ability to hit the United States as well as Europe). The United States and NATO expressed increasing apprehension about this, and a decision to produce neutron bombs remained in abeyance throughout the remainder of Carter's presidency.

The administration made an effort to downplay the magnitude of the political catastrophe it had suffered at home and abroad. Harold Brown now described the neutron bomb as "useful militarily" but said that it would not make a "decisive difference." There were "other ways to do the same thing," said the Secretary. But there were no other ways, and Brown knew this. The use of nuclear fission weapons, which constitute NATO's tactical nuclear stockpile, does not eliminate significant blast damage to urban structures. These are weapons that will both kill soldiers *and* destroy property. Only by using nuclear fusion weapons, which employ the neutron bomb principle, is it possible to put such great emphasis on radiation that the blast can be effectively removed from the target area.

If the Russians had been secretly pleased with Carter's decision, which had been in no small way influenced by their tremendous propaganda barrage† and threats to stop SALT

* When West Germany's Chancellor Helmut Schmidt (who had quietly agreed to support the Bomb) was told by a Carter emissary of Carter's decision, which sandbagged Schmidt but good, he dispatched his foreign minister, Hans-Dietrich Genscher, to the White House to plead that the decision be canceled. Genscher returned to Bonn empty-handed. According to the German weekly news magazine *Der Spiegel,* Genscher reported to the Schmidt cabinet that he found the President irrational about NATO policy, he was unable to understand the reasons for his decision, he was a "religious daydreamer."

† President Reagan stated in 1981 that the Soviets pumped more than one hundred million dollars into their anti-N-bomb campaign.

From Herblock On All Fronts (*New American Library, 1980*)

negotiations, they openly professed not to be very pacified. Leonid Brezhnev called Carter's decision "at best a half-measure." He repeated a long-standing Soviet offer to forswear neutron bomb production if the United States did the same. "I can inform you," said Brezhnev, "that we have taken the President's statement into account and that we, too, will not begin production so long as the United States does not do so. Further development will depend on Washington."

The problem is that any agreement, tacit or explicit, to effect a mutual forswearing of N-bomb production is nonsense. There is no conceivable way, by means of national technical verification, that such an agreement could be monitored. We have never known what specific kinds of nuclear weapons the Soviets have been putting into their arsenal. This would be doubly true for the neutron bomb, because we have no way of determining whether the Russians have even tested such weapons. So Brezhnev's statement was nonsense, and one would assume that Carter would have been told this by his intelligence experts. But this was not the way that the President chose to rebuke the Soviets.

Instead, Carter lashed out at Brezhnev for his hypocrisy in posing an idle threat, that they—the Russians—had no use for such weapons and thus had no interest in producing them: "The Soviets know and President Brezhnev knows that the neutron weapon is designed to be used against massive and perhaps overwhelming tank forces. . . . The neutron weapons are designed to equalize that inequality. . . . The Soviets have no use for a neutron weapon, so the offer by Brezhnev to refrain from building the neutron weapon has no significance in the European theater and he knows this." The Commander-in-Chief having said so, his lieutenants joined in poking at the Soviet perfidy. So did European spokesmen. And so did most of the media editorialists, even those who just a few weeks earlier had blasted Carter for refusing to build the Bomb. Rally 'round the flag boys, the Prez is talking back to the rotten Russian Commies, telling them off for trying to con Uncle Sam.

But Carter seemed to be living in an unreal world of his own assumptions (or really the assumptions fed to him by his key advisors) in dealing with the neutron bomb. When his administration claimed earlier that the N-bomb had been designed

C. P. Houston, The Houston Chronicle

'What's fair? You don't develop weapons to ruin our tanks; we don't build weapons to ruin our tanks'

exclusively as a defensive weapon to hold back a Soviet armored invasion of Europe, this was at odds with the truth of the matter, as I've pointed out. Besides being illogical, his remarks were downright patronizing: who was he, or any other American president for that matter (Reagan has since pulled the same stunt), to tell the Russians what was good for them or not good for them?

Anyway, defensive forces consist of people just like offensive forces. If NATO's defensive forces are going to push the Soviet forces out of European territory they have taken, which ought to be a great deal of territory in view of the Soviet conventional force preponderance, won't NATO have to go on the offensive? Or is NATO going to negotiate the Russians out of Europe? Or if NATO does try to kick the Russians out of Europe, are NATO forces going to deny themselves neutron bombs because the U.S. government said these weapons were only useful for defense?

This really had to be patently ridiculous, and yet practically nobody was willing or wanted to point this out to Carter.

That is, practically nobody, except for myself (and please excuse this immodesty). Years before this fatuous remark was made about what bombs were no good for the Soviets, I had examined the military rationale for Soviet neutron weapons requirements and determined to my satisfaction that they had excellent reasons for testing and stockpiling such weapons. Immediately upon reading Carter's remarks, I sat down and wrote an article to this point. It appeared to no avail in *The Los Angeles Times,* a newspaper of some import. I received not one response. Later on that year, in the fall of 1978, I wrote still another article, in the *International Herald Tribune,* still to no avail.

Here we have a prime example of how the government can fabricate and distort a nuclear weapons issue when it has made a boo-boo and wants to salvage some of the mess by shifting to an attack on the bad guys, in this case, the Soviets. An inverse "Red" herring, so to speak: the Russians *aren't* coming with the feared superneutron weapons, because they're not allowed (by U.S. fiat) to use the weapons. But what about all the guys in Washington, and all the newspapers around the land, who were saying fifteen or sixteen years before that if we didn't develop the neutron bomb first, the Russians would? None of these guys ever said that the Soviets had no use for N-bombs. To the contrary, they intimated that if the Soviets were to get them first, there goes the Free World. That is, they said this until we signed the Atmospheric Test Ban Treaty and backed away from a comprehensive treaty. But now many of these guys who were still around have gone down the line with Carter.

If you sense a certain intolerance on my part with regard to this political flimflammery, it's only because practically all these fellows who jump back and forth along nuclear political lines have told us that nuclear war would be the most horrible of horribles, the end of the world, and all that. Yet look at the way these guys act on what they believe to be a critical nuclear weapons issue. My tolerance for such political horseplay has indeed diminished, but good.

And you can imagine my dismay when the Reagan administration decided to build, but not *deploy,* neutron bombs, and

Interlandi Los Angeles Times

sought to justify the decision and stress its importance by repeating the same stuff that came out of the Carter administration. I'll give you a guess. Were Brezhnev to make still another announcement and say that the Russians have decided to start building neutron warheads and stockpiling them, but not with front-line troops in East Germany and Czechoslovakia, I'd guess that the U.S. government would say that they were simply trying to bluff us, since, after all, they never have had any use for these weapons. The government would call the Russian bluff and once again get cheered for it.

* * *

Now let's step back a bit and review the situation. In October of 1978, President Carter ordered the production of the fusion "components" for the N-bomb but again delayed on a production decision. This decision satisfied many of those who had been dissatisfied earlier. Carter could claim that the door was still open, the program was on the rails and an actual production decision would be made later on. But it never was. The neutron monkey was off Carter's back for a while, and he could get on to other matters unmolested.

A month later President Brezhnev produced what should have been a shocker, but wasn't, when, in November 1978, he revealed to a group of U.S. senators visiting in Moscow that "many years ago," the Russians had tested the N-bomb. "We tested," said Brezhnev, "but we never started production of that weapon." If Brezhnev were telling the truth, in all probability he was lying. The Russians don't test lightly or capriciously. They test when a given test will enhance their military capabilities, which will in turn implement their state doctrine, which stems from the old-time religion of Marx and Lenin. If indeed they had tested (I think they did it with damned good reason), then they probably did so with an eye toward production, assuming the test worked out well—which Brezhnev's remarks indicated was the case. But then, few American politicians, to say nothing about academicians, scientists and the like, have ever been able to look through the looking glass at the Soviets to see what they, the Soviets, claim they are and most probably are.

By the end of 1978 the neutron bomb had just about as much of a future in the United States and for NATO as it had during the Kennedy administration. The cost of developing the neutron (fusion) components was essentially inconsequential. The real money involved the (approved) production of the (nasty, destructive, contaminating) fission warheads, which was proceeding apace. As during the Kennedy administration, the Bomb remained in limbo.

Had Carter won the election in 1980, limbo would probably have been crystallized into a state of rigor mortis, and the neutron bomb would have been consigned to a potter's field. This didn't turn out to be the case, however. Ronald Reagan, who had been excoriating Carter for his handling of the neutron bomb, and

Reprinted by permission of Tribune Company Syndicate, Inc.

whose party platform had pretty well pledged its production, was elected. Not long after Reagan moved to Washington, Washington was again involved in political debate over the Bomb. Our NATO allies again became edgy. They had been badly burned once and they weren't about to stick their feet into the fire again.

On February 3, 1981, Reagan's Defense Secretary, Caspar Weinberger, said in a news conference that the United States would "very probably" want to deploy neutron weapons in Europe. Weinberger said that President Carter was right in backing deployment originally, but went wrong when he pulled away. Trying to justify his opinion, the Secretary claimed that the West Germans would welcome a deployment decision: "We have had, in the very recent past, a strong recommendation from this government [West Germany] that it be used. I so far have seen very little to indicate to my mind that was wrong . . . So I think the opportunity that this weapon gives to strengthen theater nuclear forces is one that we very probably would want to make use of." However, Weinberger added that regarding actual deployment to Europe, "we would certainly want to consult with all our allies and friends."

Suddenly, however, Weinberger found himself leading a neutron crusade of one.

The State Department moved quickly to disassociate itself from the remarks coming from the Pentagon across the Potomac. Alexander Haig sent a message to NATO members assuring them that Weinberger's remarks in no way implied that an N-bomb production decision had been made by the Reagan administration. Moreover, the State Department also made clear that first things had to be done first. Before moving on neutron bombs, the problem of deploying the so-called "Euromissiles" (Pershing II ballistic missiles and intermediate-range ground-launched cruise missiles) had to be taken care of. This was seconded by the Chairman of the JCS, who also warned that moving too quickly on N-bombs would jeopardize the deployment of Euromissiles.

There was immediate protest in Europe over Weinberger's statement. West Germany now allowed that its former position of acceptance of neutron weapons had changed. A German spokesman, Klaus Becker, referred to Weinberger's statement as "a vague formulation," adding that the previous German support "doesn't exist anymore."

Meanwhile, the Russians dusted off old propaganda statements and reissued them in slightly updated form. Once again they warned the Europeans that "production and deployment of neutron weapons on the territory of Western Europe can only seriously worsen the situation on the European continent and draw it into a new round of the arms race with all its dangers and special risks for the densely populated countries of Western Europe." (TASS, February 3).

There was certainly no great enthusiasm in Congress for immediately producing neutron bombs. The general feeling of key legislators was that the Euromissiles should be given first priority. For example, Senator John Tower (R-Texas), chairman of the Senate Armed Services Committee, said that he had advised Reagan that "perhaps we shouldn't press right now on [the neutron bomb] because of political problems. The point is that Mr. Carter's handling of that issue has made it politically very difficult for us in Western Europe, and the priority is the modernization of tactical nuclear forces [i.e., Euromissiles] in that area." This advice was just about the opposite tendered by Senator Tower two months earlier, when he had said that neutron weapons "should be produced and deployed. Helmut Schmidt had already gained acceptance [of deployment on German soil] and

Carter sawed his limb off by scrubbing the project. That hurt Schmidt." Apparently the senator had found out that the chancellor had no desire this time to be helped by the U.S. deployment of N-bombs on his territory.

Almost as quickly as it had begun, the revival of the neutron bomb issue subsided. As if to show that he wasn't backing away from the backlash to his initial remarks, Caspar Weinberger continued briefly to uphold the Bomb's military virtues: "When you look at the number of Russian tanks and the other items, the [neutron] warhead could do quite a lot to restore some kind of balance there. And I believe that's one of the reasons the Russians are reacting so strongly to this slight suggestion." He also made it clear that he continued to favor its deployment, stating that the weapon "adds a great deal to the strength from a number of points of view, one of which is deterrence . . . I think it's a very good addition." Despite this firm reavowal by Weinberger, however, the issue slid beneath the surface. It was announced that an executive branch interagency review group was being established to evaluate the issue (a standard stall, when an imminent decision becomes inadvisable for political reasons). Any action on the Bomb would have to await the review group's findings and recommendations, which are sometimes accepted and sometimes not. During this brief brouhaha, there was not one firm indication of where the White House stood on this issue.

On August 8, 1981, it was announced from Santa Barbara, where President Reagan had just begun a vacation at his ranch, that the President had decided to produce neutron warheads. However, the decision specified that the warheads would be stockpiled solely in the United States; any deployment in Europe would take place only after consultation with European allies.

Apparently, at a White House meeting attended by the President just prior to his departure for the ranch, he had heard the final arguments of the two principal factions. Haig maintained, as he had previously, that the Euromissiles had to come first; an N-bomb decision would unduly risk the Euromissile program. He also maintained that a decision would heighten European fears about limited nuclear war in Europe. Weinberger took the position that the United States should not allow itself to be dominated by European attitudes. He saw no signs that the Euromissile situation would soon be resolved. Thus, he saw no reason to wait any longer on producing N-bombs. He turned out to be dead right. In fact, for reasons having relatively little to do with the neutron bomb, the Euromissile situation began to fall apart at the seams as antinuclear demonstrations spread across Europe. As these words are written, prospects for these missiles being deployed are about as good as prospects for balancing the U.S. budget by 1984.

The upshot was that Haig lost totally, since he was against doing anything, and Weinberger picked up a lease with a possible option to buy—including buying a home for these weapons someplace other than Europe. At one point after the President's decision was made, the Defense Secretary said that military application was not confined to Europe, sensibly pulling away from the disinformation of our hard-sell approach to the Europeans. This should have raised a few eyebrows, including those of the President, who said a couple of days later in a press conference: "This weapon was particularly designed to offset the great superiority that the Soviet Union has on the Western front against the NATO nations."

Politically, one might say that the President acted courageously in deciding to build the Bomb without checking out his decision with NATO allies. Had he done so, he would have gotten himself conned into an indefinite delay. This, of course, has been the story of U.S. consultations with NATO European countries from the beginning.

All NATO has wanted, and thus far the United States seems to have been more than glad to oblige, is for us to keep up our strategic nuclear pledges, praying that this is the magic formula for peace, but nothing more. These countries certainly haven't wanted to create a realistic ground defense, for one simple reason: They don't want to be in a position to have to fight another long, drawn-out ground war. They've already had two of these this century. That's enough. Furthermore, it wouldn't make any difference if they bolstered their conventional defenses; the Soviets will use nuclear weapons. They have conniption fits at the thought of improving NATO's nuclear weapons—especially those for directly defending Europe.

'THANK YOU, DR. WEINBERGER. I THINK WE'LL CALL HIM NEUTRON.'

For the sake of the "Alliance" (a term that, in the U.S. foreign policy establishment, has taken on more sacred proportions than the Holy Trinity), the United States has chosen to go along with this garbage. In so doing, with each passing day America is pushing itself to the brink of suicide. NATO is no longer a credible military pact. It is now an arrangement where if the war were to start, the United States would be committing physical suicide (because we are completely vulnerable to nuclear attack), and the Europeans, if they could pull it off (and they'd sure want to try), would only have committed political suicide. They would have been occupied by Communist armies, but they would have avoided physical suicide by not fighting. This is, in effect, what they're trying to accomplish: refusing to be put in a position where they can put up a credible fight.

So what else is new? For centuries European countries have been swallowed up by other European countries. To have been conquered and lived to fight again another day is par for the course over there. But our country has never been in this position before. It is not in our national genes to play this way. And we certainly don't want to get ourselves killed—politically and physically—which is going to happen the way we are going.

With this discussion in mind, if President Reagan was courageous in bucking Allied sensitivities, and those of the U.S. Establishment that so desperately caters to these sensitivities, was he as courageous as he might, and perhaps should, have been?

What I'm driving at here is another set of sensitivities that must exist, but which seems to have been buried deep in the American psyche. These are the sensitivities having to do with our military involvement with the Europeans, whom we bailed out in World War II, helped enormously to rebuild after the war, saved from Communist conquest by establishing NATO and supplying the nuclear muscle for all these years, and who steadfastly continue to resist all our efforts to provide them with improved nuclear defense and to get them to improve their nonnuclear forces. These are the Europeans who, during the Vietnam War, while we sought to protect non-Communist Asians from Communist conquest, jeered us from the sidelines and had the gall to complain that our efforts there were weakening NATO defenses.

Until recently, I've been one of those who went on worshiping the sacred cow of NATO and believing in my political leaders. But no longer. And in this connection I'd like to ask my fearless leaders in Washington: Hey! Why are you guys telling me that the neutron bomb is the greatest thing since sliced bread, that it will hold back the hordes of Russian tanks and do so without demolishing our allies and their economy, yet you're afraid to ship N-bombs over to Europe because of European sensitivities? If you guys are really right about this wonder weapon, why is it that a couple of hundred thousand American troops over there aren't being protected by these weapons? Why do you guys show all that courage about defying the Europeans on something we deploy here in America, but cave in on something we should be morally bound to do over there? Why don't we protect the American forces who are over there to protect the Europeans with the best weapons available?

A few days after Reagan's N-bomb production decision was made, Caspar Weinberger wrote an explanation and a defense of the decision in *The Washington Post.* His explanation included the following comments:

> Suppose that it were possible to increase the military effectiveness of a battlefield weapon and, at the same time, reduce substantially the number of civilians who would be

> killed by its use just because they were unlucky enough to live near where the war was taking place.
>
> Suppose further, that the weapon were designed to stop a massive invasion by enemy armor that might otherwise roll, in blitzkrieg fashion, across democratic Europe and the territory of our principal allies.
>
> Suppose, finally, that in addition to the weapon's ability to help blunt an invasion of Europe and save thousands of innocent civilian lives, it was safer, had increased range and better security. . . .
>
> Neutron weapons, which President Reagan has decided to produce, have precisely these characteristics. Moreover, they have a crucial characteristic that is more important than anything else about them, they would reduce the likelihood that, even in a crisis, the Soviets would be tempted to launch an attack on our European allies. They thus promise to add to the credibility of our deterrent, and because they do that, they actually reduce the likelihood that nuclear weapons would ever be used in a European war.
>
> The President's decision to produce and stockpile neutron weapons on U.S. territory is intended to strike a prudent balance between European sensitivities, on the one hand, and, on the other, the necessity to make difficult decisions affecting U.S. forces on their own merits.

I can draw only one conclusion from the Secretary's explanation: We should pull our military forces out of Europe.

If the neutron bomb has the tremendous attributes Weinberger claims, the most important of all being its contribution to deterring war, then on what conceivable grounds would we be willing to put up with European sensitivities? If the deployment of neutron weapons to Europe, replacing the unacceptable, dirty, destructive weapons now there, would serve this noble purpose of deterrence, on what conceivable grounds could the Europeans legitimately refuse to accept such deployment? That is, unless they just don't want any nuclear defense at all, which I'm afraid is the case. And if this is the case, since there is no conceivable way to defend Europe without nuclear weapons, then we should probably collect our nuclear marbles over there and ship them home. If we did this, however, we would be leaving American forces totally at the mercy of the Russians, so we might as well bring home everything, kit and caboodle. Our forces are over there for one basic reason, to help defend Europe. They are not there as hostages to Soviet aggression.

Trying to rationalize the decision to store the neutron warheads in the United States, Weinberger said that the warheads could be delivered to troops in Western Europe within "only a few hours," *after* approval is obtained from NATO allies. But that's putting the cart before the horse. If keeping the weapons in the U.S. is in deference to Allied disapproval of having them in Europe, because they're afraid they might be used, then what good does it do us to say we can get them over there quickly? It just doesn't add up.

By the time President Reagan's neutron bomb decision was announced, NATO European countries had become far more concerned about the Euromissiles they had agreed to accept than the neutron weapons they were told they wouldn't have to accept if they didn't want to. The antinuclear marches that commenced were directed more against Euromissiles than N-bombs. Perhaps the best way to sum up the European reaction is in the words of a Socialist member of the Italian government who said: "Any new bomb is bad news."

To be sure, there were complaints about the timing of Reagan's decision, for the reasons Secretary of State Alexander Haig had predicted: It threatened to foul up European efforts to come to terms with nuclear weapons. They were being overloaded with nukes.

The editor of Germany's *Die Zeit,* Theo Summer (long an associate of Helmut Schmidt), wrote in *The Washington Post* on Reagan's decision:

> It ignores fundamental issues of NATO's strategic doctrine, and it reveals a lack of diplomatic, political and psychological finesse reminiscent of the worst moments of the Carter years.... The European antinuclear lobby is already campaigning against NATO's decision to modernize NATO's theater nuclear forces. The revival of the neutron debate can only make life more difficult for the 5 embattled governments that are prepared to station 572 Pershing II and cruise missiles in their countries . . .

On the other hand, the German government was much more restrained. A government spokesman explained that the decision was an "exclusively American affair," since the warheads were to be based "exclusively on U.S. territory." After a while even Schmidt backed away somewhat from the resistance his government had shown earlier in the year and declared that he had not really changed his mind from 1978, when "we said that we could envisage the stationing on German soil—which at the present time is not urgent and over which there are presently no negotiations—only under very explicit conditions [that other NATO nations store N-bombs too, and if arms control efforts with the Soviets fail—pretty safe conditions]."

In the Netherlands some thirty Dutch demonstrators gathered outside the U.S. Embassy and demanded that the Bomb be banned. This was a far cry from forty thousand marching in the rain through Amsterdam a few years before. And though the Dutch government issued a statement lamenting the fact that the NATO European allies had not been informed earlier about the U.S. decision, *that* was a far cry from what happened a few years earlier when, in the face of violent domestic opposition to the N-bomb, the government almost fell for not rejecting it outright.

In the USSR the standard denunciations were dusted off and played once more. Following an interview I gave on Dutch TV in the spring of 1981, *Pravda* wrote that I loved my bomb more than my older son, who was in the navy: "Think about this . . . With great eloquence, he [Sam Cohen] truly displayed the dreadful moral degradation of those American scientists who have sold their minds to the Pentagon. His fatherly feelings toward the neutron bomb he created turned out to be stronger than his concern for his own son, who could come to his death if and when this new weapon is introduced into the arsenal of war."

In Kuwait a newspaper editorial dragged me into an American-Israeli plot to take over the Gulf's oil. "America's fears focus on Gulf oil," said the editorial, adding that the Arabs are afraid that the United States might "remember Nagasaki" when trying to cop the oil supply. (That is a good point, I might say. If we wanted the oil badly enough and the Arabs were giving us trouble, the use of neutron bombs, if we valued oil over Arabs, would be the ideal solution. The Russians would be right: It would be a real capitalist weapon.) But the plot thickened. I was a Jew. Obviously I was in cahoots with both the Americans and the Israelis. The editorial continued: "The Father of the Neutron Bomb is named 'Cohen.' Israel attacks Arabs and murders Arab citizens with American weapons, and 'Cohen,' with all this name implies, continues to design deadly 'clean weapons.' "

So it's now 1983. The neutron bomb issue seems to have entered another period of dormancy. Somewhere in the United States, the bombs are being stored. But for what ultimate disposition, I do not know.

CHAPTER 5 THE FIRST NEUTRON BOMB BRIEFING

A FEW YEARS AFTER MY neutron bomb road show came to an end, sometime in the mid-1960's, I got a call from a person at RAND who worried about the storage of classified material. My briefing charts, which were pretty big and bulky, were using up valuable storage space in the vault. Would I ever have need of them again? If not, would it be okay if they were shoved into the furnace to be cremated along with other classified waste on hand?

It seemed highly improbable to me that I would ever be called upon to give another N-bomb performance (which turned out to be the case). What the heck, I thought. "Go ahead and burn them," I told her. So the charts, which had helped create a bit of history, were reduced to ashes.

Ironically, in pondering how to write this chapter—which deals with how neutron bombs work, what they do and don't do, and with defending the bomb's technical virtues against technical critics, I thought it would be a good idea to begin the way I started some twenty-five years ago, with the first neutron bomb briefing. I'm getting older and more forgetful of events from my ancient past (my batting average for remembering my wedding anniversary is so low, and my wife is becoming so angry at me for forgetting, that I fear our next one may be our last one). This being the state of my memory, what I'll now present won't be exactly what I first presented. But it will be a reasonable facsimile. So here we go:

"Gentlemen [I don't recall any ladies being present in the audience; nuclear war was a man's world in those days], I would like to present to you a new concept for battlefield nuclear weapons to be used in limited wars against nonnuclear Asian Communist enemies. This could be pushing back and defeating aggression in such places as Korea and Southeast Asia, where limited wars can be anticipated. This concept will be based on using the nuclear radiation that is emitted instantaneously at the time of burst to kill and incapacitate enemy personnel. If we accept nuclear radiation as a kill mechanism, not only can we obtain a more effective class of battlefield nuclear weapons, but we can achieve a degree of discrimination not possible with current stockpile weapons and also not possible with conventional high-explosive weapons. Let me begin by showing the essential difference between using this new class of weapons and using those now in the battlefield stockpile. [The first chart is placed on the easel.]

"Our current battlefield nuclear weapons operate on the same physical principle as the atomic bombs that were dropped on Hiroshima and Nagasaki. They are based on nuclear *fission,* a process that involves splitting the nuclei of the heaviest of the elements, such as uranium and plutonium. (The bomb that destroyed Hiroshima used uranium; the one that destroyed Naga-

FISSION

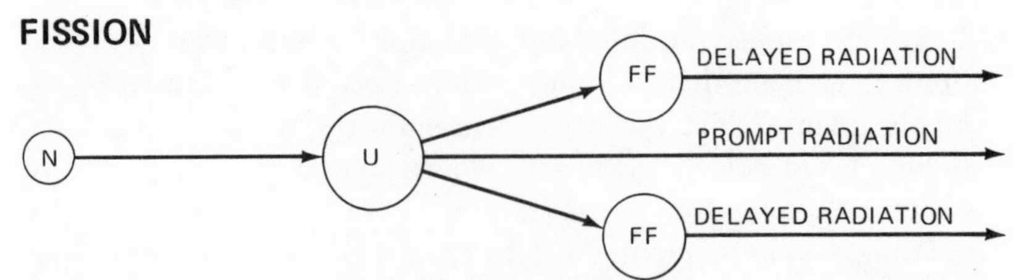

ENERGY PARTITION: 85% BLAST AND HEAT, 10% DELAYED RADIATION, 5% PROMPT RADIATION

FUSION

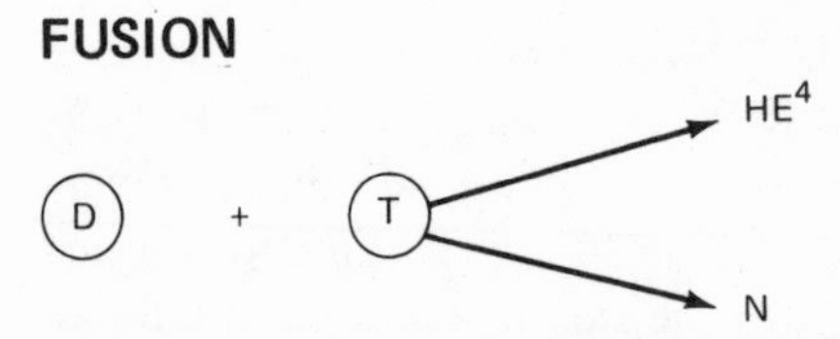

ENERGY PARTITION: 80% PROMPT RADIATION, 20% BLAST + HEAT

saki used plutonium.) The actual fissioning is caused by the nucleus absorbing a neutron. This causes the nucleus to become unstable and split into two parts.

"In the process of fissioning, the nucleus breaks up into two lighter nuclei and, at the same time, emits gamma rays and neutrons. Some of these neutrons are absorbed by fissile nuclei to cause more fissioning, i.e., to keep the "chain reaction" going; others escape into the surroundings. The two lighter nuclei, called *fission fragments,* are radioactive and constitute the source of *radioactive fallout,* which can produce wide-scale contamination lasting centuries.

"Most of the energy release of a fission explosion goes into the fission fragments. These charged atomic particles are instantly absorbed by the weapon material itself. This causes the weapon material to become unbelievably hot. This causes the immediate surroundings (usually air) to get very hot. Very hot air creates very high pressure, which then produces a very high pressure pulse—the blast wave. The temperature of the air gets so high that it glows like the sun for a while (this is the "fireball" we have seen so often in photographs) and emits heat known technically as thermal radiation. The combination of the shock, or blast (which can knock down buildings) and the heat (which can set buildings on fire and scorch exposed people) is the result of about eighty-five percent of a fission bomb's energy.

"Of the remaining energy, ten percent goes into radiation emitted by the radioactive fission fragments. Another five percent goes into gamma rays and neutrons emitted essentially at the time of burst. Having no electrical charge, the gamma rays and neutrons can go considerable distances in the air. They kill and incapacitate people. Humans are extremely sensitive to radiation energy; far more sensitive than they are to blast and heat. On the battlefield, because of this great human sensitivity to radiation, even though most of the energy goes into heat and blast, the radiation effects can still be very effective against exposed military personnel. In essence, a fission bomb is a bomb that both kills people and demolishes property.

"The concept of the neutron bomb operates on the same physical principle as the hydrogen bomb. Specifically it relies on nuclear *fusion,* a process that involves the combining, or fusing, of the nuclei of the very lightest of elements: hydrogen. It involves the fusing of two kinds of heavy hydrogen: deuterium (the hydrogen component of heavy water) and tritium (the heaviest form of hydrogen, which is not found in nature and must be produced in nuclear reactors). To cause nuclear fusion to occur on a macroscopic scale, the hydrogen nuclei must be brought together under conditions of enormous temperature and pressure. In current hydrogen bombs this is accomplished by using a fission explosive, popularly called the *trigger,* to engender these conditions. When the fusion of these hydrogen nuclei occurs, there are two products: helium nuclei (identical to what exists in our atmosphere) and neutrons of very high energy, far more energetic than neutrons caused by fission. And we note from the chart that fusion does not produce any radioactivity.

"In contrast to fission weapons, most of the fusion energy goes into the neutrons; about eighty percent. The remainder, twenty percent, goes into the helium nuclei, which, being charged particles, are all absorbed in the weapon and create its blast and heat. The accent on instantaneous nuclear radiation in the fusion weapon concept gives it an antipersonnel effectiveness equivalent to that of an A-bomb that possesses about twenty times as much explosive power, but has less than one-twentieth the output of blast and heat of the A-bomb. In other words, a one-kiloton fusion weapon can reach out from ground zero to neutralize enemy soldiers at the same distance as would a twenty-kiloton A-bomb, the bomb that destroyed Nagasaki, but with a subkiloton blast and heat power.* Thus, we have a reversal of energy partition in going from A-bombs to fusion bombs. In a bit, I'll get into the significance and implications of these uniquely different characteristics of battlefield fusion weapons. First, however, I'd like to describe two specific warhead designs that pretty well cover the waterfront of possibilities for this new concept.

"The first design represents something we are sure we know how to do, since we already have had considerable experience along these lines. This is a so-called fission-fusion design that employs a fission trigger to produce the necessary conditions of temperature and pressure to "burn" the deuterium and tritium in the second stage. It will create the fusion reactions I've just described, which in turn will give rise to a tremendous burst of high-energy neutrons. We envisage this device to have a yield at the one-kiloton level. Were the United States to resume nuclear testing, we feel that a warhead of this type could be developed quickly.

"The second design represents a much more formidable challenge. We've never done anything like this before. Were we to be successful in such a development, this would represent a great breakthrough in nuclear weapons. The design is directed toward achieving what we call a "pure-fusion" warhead: that is, a warhead that contains no fissile material whatsoever. Such a warhead would not produce any significant levels of radioactivity. This, from a psychological standpoint, could greatly enhance political acceptability. [This last point turned out to be a lot of malarky since, when the Kennedy administration came in, all nuclear weapons, regardless of their specific characteristics, were regarded as politically unacceptable—and still are.] Also of critical importance is the fact that this design offers the opportunity to have nuclear weapons whose explosive power can be identified with that of large high-explosive bombs—like the "blockbusters" we used in World War II. However, unlike high-explosive bombs, they could be used against enemy forces without destroying large areas of urban property, as I'll demonstrate shortly. Finally I would point out that the pure-fusion weapon would probably re-

* This is the technical basis of the weapons effectiveness charts.

quire an extremely small amount of costly nuclear material. Thus, the cost constraint associated with weapons that use fissile materials almost disappears. We can envisage very high production levels of these weapons for extensive battlefield use. However, being far more effective than high-explosive weapons, the production levels of these pure-fusion weapons would be far below those required for high-explosive conventional warfare.

"Next I will put up a chart that shows the extent of instantaneous radiation effects against military personnel, and blast effects against urban structures, for the two warhead designs just described, and for a twenty-kiloton (Nagasaki-size) fission bomb. I'm leaving out the heat effects against structures for two reasons: (1) They are generally less effective (in producing combustion) than blast (to level buildings), and (2) They are very sensitive in extent to atmospheric conditions, and thus do not constitute a reliable yardstick for estimating urban damage. [Up goes Chart II.]

"Let's first compare the one-kiloton fission-fusion warhead with a twenty-kiloton fission bomb. In both cases the weapons are exploded close to the surface, just high enough so that there is no danger of making a crater, which would result in a lot of soil, containing most of the bomb's radioactivity, being carried up into the air and then coming down as radioactive fallout (which could well affect our own troops as well as the civilian population). The slanted bars show the extent of the radiation that would neutralize military personnel; the solid black bars show the extent of the blast effects that would destroy urban structures.

"As I explained, both weapons are equally effective for use against military personnel, reaching out about a thousand yards from ground zero. But note the difference in the extent of urban destruction: The blast of the twenty-kiloton fission bomb reaches out to nearly fifteen hundred yards, well beyond the radiation radius. The blast of the one-kiloton fission-fusion warhead reaches out about six hundred yards. It is well within the radiation radius. So, for one-twentieth the explosive power of the bomb that destroyed Nagasaki, this new weapon concept allows the same military effectiveness. But it reduces the blast-destruction radius by two thirds (which means that the area of destruction is reduced by about ninety percent—a very large reduction).

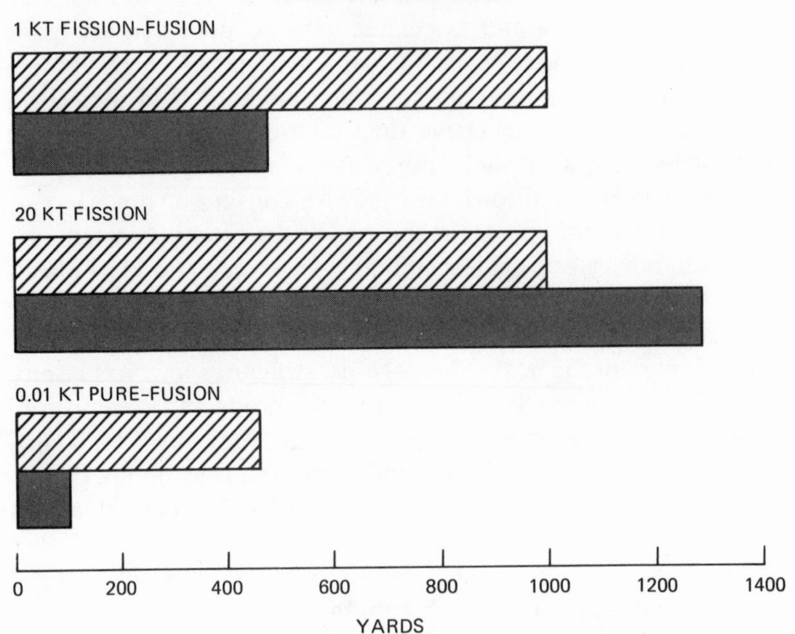

"However, we can do even better than that if we explode the fission-fusion warhead high above the ground. [This was the fundamental discovery I made when I made my original neutron bomb calculations.] Let me demonstrate this by removing the weapon-effects bars from the chart [they were thick cardboard strips mounted on the chart by little screws, one at each end].

"Let's imagine that a limited war someplace has become involved in pushing the enemy out of a city that belongs to an ally of ours, as was the case of Seoul in the Korean War. (I now put up Chart III on a second easel. This is a poor man's skyline of a metropolitan area, which consists of a number of staggered rooftops.)

"Now, I first want to screw in the ground-zero point of the fission-fusion warhead-effects bar at a height over a city and swing it around to see what happens down below. What we observe is that we can flood much of the city area with radiation that will knock out the enemy troops. But that at the same time we will not knock out the city itself, since destructive blast pressures will not reach down that far. So, with this new concept we have for the

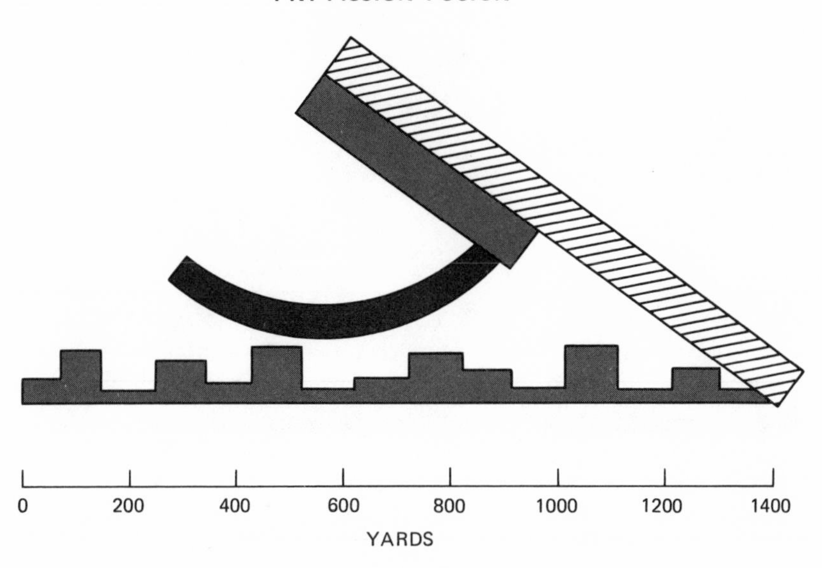

first time a weapon that can destroy the enemy in a city it occupies, but not at the same time destroy the city. With this new weapon concept we have achieved a new dimension for ground warfare.

"Can we accomplish this with a fission bomb? The answer is: No. To prove the point, I swivel the twenty-kiloton fission bomb bar high above the city. Look what happens: We not only destroy the enemy forces with radiation, but we destroy the city as well.

"Next I'll swivel the ten-ton yield pure-fusion weapon over the city. Like the fission-fusion weapon, it too can kill the enemy while not destroying property. Its principal virtue is that it offers a more discriminate capability and a greater degree of flexibility. Not all target areas are going to be two thousand yards in radius. In fact, it can be expected that enemy troops, in their efforts to survive nuclear attacks, will probably disperse into small groups, continually on the move. This would call for a very large number of weapons, each with very low explosive power—i.e., pure-fusion weapons. And one notes, as I swivel the bar, that this weapon deemphasizes blast even more than the fission-fusion warhead. [This is the weapon—pure-fusion—that had the navy guys excited. It was their chance to push the air force (and maybe the

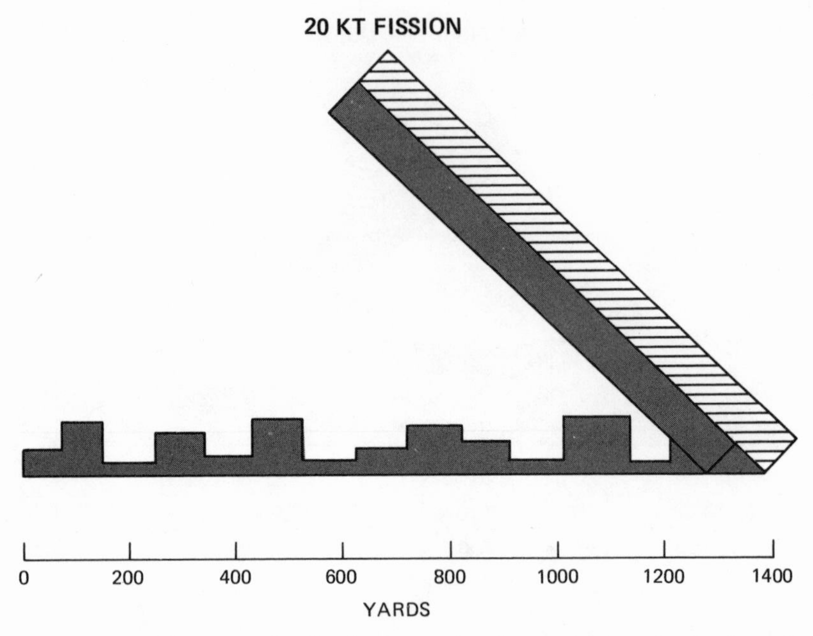

army as well) out of the limited-war business. If they had piles of these things on every carrier, on station and ready to go at a moment's notice, the marines could do the mopping up.] It can fairly be said that having such a capability would represent the ultimate in discriminate nuclear weapons as we now understand them.

"Well, gentlemen, this concludes my briefing. Are there any questions?"

This, then, is essentially how the first neutron bomb briefing went. There were a few other odds and ends that I commented on. The most important of those being that N-bombs would substantially improve the safety problem of friendly troops, in that our soldiers could be significantly closer to the nuclear burst so that they could more effectively exploit the attack. However, the real punch line of the briefing was swiveling the bars to show that for the first time we could have a weapon that could remove a scourge of the past: the wholesale devastation of populated areas.

Being able to kill enemy soldiers without destroying civilian property adds a new dimension to ground warfare that civilized nations have sought over the ages but could never achieve. The specter of cities lying in ruins after being bitterly contested in conventional high-explosive warfare can become a thing of the

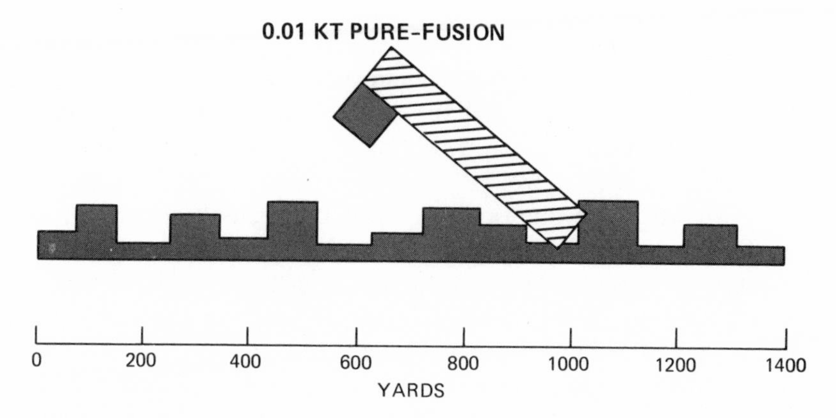

past. The civilian population does not have to be decimated. The enemy, not being able to take a city and exploit it both militarily and politically (as has been traditional in conventional war) without becoming a neutron bomb target, should be deterred from wanting to take the city. If he insists upon trying to take it anyway, there would be no need to defend it in a classical way, thereby inviting urban devastation. Rather, the ploy would be to let him go right ahead, keep your own forces away and "nuke" him with neutron bombs.

The question of what happens to civilians living in the city deserves further comment. Their situation becomes far more viable when neutron bombs enter the picture. All they have to do is construct very simple radiation shelters and, as the enemy approaches, get into them. At a cost of approximately one hundred dollars per occupant, these shelters would be very cheap to construct. Because there is no blast to contend with in the shelter design, all that is called for is piling several feet of earth over the shelter. And dirt is cheap. Surely this would be a solution toward removing the civilians from the war, which is far preferable to evacuation as the enemy approaches. All the problems and misery that go with refugees clogging up the roads, frequently coming under fire, wondering how they are going to survive and what they might be coming back to after the war can be avoided.

Now one might be a bit suspicious of such a bold claim about civilian survivability in a neutron bomb environment, and ask the following questions: 1) If the civilians can protect themselves so easily by digging in, why can't the enemy do the same thing, thereby rendering the N-bomb ineffective? and 2) Wouldn't evacuation be better for the civilians, since if the enemy digs in, we'd have to blast him out, thereby killing friend and foe alike and demolishing the city as well?

To answer these questions we must take a look at the war at hand. The Soviet strategy for invading Europe is to take it over as quickly as possible. This will be accomplished by conducting a massive, armored blitzkrieg-style assault—as the Germans did when they attacked France in World War II. The Soviet game plan is to keep moving, mounting wave after wave of armored attacks, until victory has been achieved. Were the Russian soldiers to get out of their tanks and dig in to protect themselves against the neutron effects, they would be defeating their own purposes. The invasion would quickly come to a standstill. If the Red Army wants to conquer Europe, it really has no choice but to stay on the surface and move forward as fast as its little treads and wheels can carry it.

On the other hand, the civilians, who are not compelled to race across Europe, are best off staying put and holing up in radiation shelters. If the Russian soldiers want to join them in these shelters, that would be just fine as far as NATO's military commanders are concerned, for these soldiers would have effectively taken themselves out of the Soviet blitzkrieg attack. But as I've just explained, this is not a tactic the Red Army commanders would tolerate.

Were we to stick with fission battlefield weapons for the defense of our allies, using them on our allies' territory (as we have always planned to do in the event of war) the prospects for civilian survival just discussed would disappear. Because of the high amount of energy that manifests itself in heat and blast when these weapons are exploded, there would be no way to burst them near or over European cities without extreme civil devastation and death. To one degree or another, we would be repeating the Hiroshima and Nagasaki experiences. That repetition is what our NATO allies have dreaded for many years.

In the mid-1950's NATO conducted a planning exercise called *Carte Blanche.* It examined the potential consequences of a tactical nuclear war. As the name of the exercise indicates, there was no limit on the types of weapons employed; the objective of this hypothetical war was to conduct a successful defense of Europe. It was estimated that if 268 A-bombs were detonated on West German soil during a three-day period, there would be civilian casualties of more than 1.5 million dead and 3.5 million wounded. This projected carnage caused a Bundestag member to exclaim that "the use of tactical nuclear weapons might develop into a war of annihilation that would wipe out the greater part of those living today." From that time on the Germans have had a horror image of nuclear warfare within their borders that has been impossible to erase. The neutron bomb has had no discernible impact on German opinion. Tactical nuclear warfare on their territory has remained "unthinkable."

Since the U.S. government began its campaign to convince European allies that the neutron bomb was good for them, not once has the prospect of meaningful civil defense against the effects of these weapons been held forth. To be sure, there have been statements that civilian damage could be reduced by using N-bombs, but the notion that the damage could be effectively eliminated by simple civil defense measures has never been officially advanced. Nothing has been done to refute the doomsday image held by Europeans.

During World War II the Germans poured an unbelievable amount of concrete to protect themselves against the Allied bombing attacks. They built massive concrete shelters throughout the country, which could have held up to 75 percent of the population of the principal towns and cities if it became necessary. The majority of the shelters had wall thickness of about five feet. (Hitler's personal bunker in Berlin had a roof composed of sixteen feet of concrete topped with six feet of earth.) These shelters provided very substantial protection for the German civilians and saved many thousands of lives. With such huge thicknesses of concrete to shield out nuclear radiation, they would have provided full protection against neutron bomb attacks in the vicinity.

The point to be made here is that the Germans went to an enormous amount of trouble to protect themselves from high-explosive bombs because they knew they could survive a conventional war (history had taught them that), and that such protection could save huge numbers of lives. Today, however, they have convinced themselves that it is fruitless to try to defend themselves against the effects of tactical nuclear weapons. They have an emotional blind spot that precludes their giving sober thought to such defense. Yet were they to spend but a small fraction of the effort made during the last war, they could have all the defensive benefits of neutron weapons and keep the endangered population safe. (For that matter, we Americans are no better. We have left ourselves naked against nuclear attack, even though a prudent, not-too-expensive civil defense program could save millions of lives.)

Obviously this civilian-sparing feature of the neutron bomb has made no impression on the Europeans. They still want no part of this weapon, because they don't want any part of their territory to become a nuclear battleground. However, this opposition is not totally blind and emotional. Because of what U.S. officials have told them, many Europeans oppose the N-bomb proposal for NATO by claiming: "Look, if we use these discriminate weapons, the Soviets will counter with their highly indiscriminate weapons.* Every European knows that the Soviet battlefield nuclear arsenal is full of indiscriminate weapons. You Americans told us this was so. And it will be of precious little consolation if the use of your sparing weapons brings about the use of the Russians' unsparing weapons and we are wiped out. It's damned little solace to us if we're going to be wiped out, regardless of who does the wiping out."

At first glance, this argument would seem to have a valid ring. But if one were to examine this issue in any depth, he might find good grounds for rejecting it. For the argument is specious and dangerous to European security. Later, we'll get into the matter of how the other side looks at its tactical nuclear weapons and what kinds of weapons it may have developed. For the time being though, we'll simply say that it doesn't ring true.

What neutron bombs *do* do is to cover a large area of the battlefield with instantaneous nuclear radiation that will quickly inca-

* This argument assumes that NATO will be the first to use nuclear weapons. This assumption is the cornerstone of NATO nuclear weapon strategy. It is unfounded and most probably wrong, as will be discussed in Chapter 8.

pacitate enemy soldiers but spare civilians (if they are sheltered) and their property. Theoretically, if neutron bombs are used properly, they do *not* mutilate the persons they affect, nor do they produce a huge incidence of cancer or genetic damage in those affected. And they do *not* make the area where they are used uninhabitable because of radioactive contamination. Whereas it might be regarded by many as insensitive, if not downright vulgar, to heap praise on military weapons designed to kill, by comparison with other nuclear weapons and conventional high-explosive weapons, neutron bombs do seem praiseworthy.

However, these simple technical truths about neutron bombs have still not prevented their detractors from making a number of untruthful contentions that the bombs are indeed insidious objects. In the forefront of the ranks of these detractors these days, as was the situation two decades ago, are a number of American scientists and commentators. They have made bold claims, mostly having to do with radiation, that the N-bomb does a lot of ineffective or nefarious things that, in fact, it doesn't do. Let's pick up some of these claims, for scrutiny and for an assessment of their veracity.

CLAIM NUMBER 1: ZOMBIES ARE GREAT TANKERS.

When a one-kiloton neutron bomb explodes over the battlefield it has been determined that, based on many years of pertinent radiobiological research, a supralethal, immediately incapacitating radiation dose to tank crews will extend to about one thousand yards from ground zero. At a distance of thirteen hundred yards, a lethal but not immediately incapacitating dose will accrue. It causes severe physical distress and certainly reduces military performance significantly. What this means is that there will be a significant area covered by the radiation, in which tankers will presumably be in a never-never land: They will be able to perform at less than full efficiency, but sooner or later, in a matter of days or weeks, many of them are going to die. Their predicament, a terrible one but not a unique one, is somewhat akin to a terminal phase of cancer. One feels miserable but can nevertheless perform certain physical functions up until the final decline into death occurs.

Not ever having taken the trouble to analyze this "zombie" predicament in terms of the military, physiological or psychological realities affecting the situation, a number of scientists have claimed that, realizing they're doomed to death, the zombies (the "walking dead") will turn into combat tigers and fight even more efficiently than if they had never been irradiated.* For example, Herbert Scoville, Jr., who held key technical jobs in the Pentagon, the CIA and the Arms Control Agency, recently claimed that the tankers that fall into this lethal, but not totally disabling irradiation category will be able to recover from the initial distress and fight like "a Kamikaze" for hours or days, depending on how big a dose they received.

What Scoville has done here is to divert the targeting issue to troops that aren't targeted by the army. He *then* claims that it nullifies the effectiveness of the weapon. He's pulled the old strawman trick.

What the army does when it tries to figure out how to attack a nuclear target is to determine what the weapon requirement is for knocking out a certain fraction of the enemy unit. Combat history over the centuries shows that, depending on the military situation at hand, if a certain fraction of a unit can be put out of action, the unit itself is effectively neutralized. To continue the battle in a fast-moving war, a fresh unit has to be sent in. In fact, this is exactly what the Soviets intend to do in a battlefield nuclear war. Their strategy is to go like hell, and if a unit commander decides that his outfit is no longer capable of pushing forward with maximum effectiveness, to the rear they go and up comes a re-

* How those irradiated will be able to determine whether they have joined the ranks of the zombies is never explained. It is just as well, because there is no credible explanation. The variation in human sensitivity to radiation is so large that a dose fatal to one person may only be injurious to another; and no individual has the wildest idea where he is on the distribution curve. Furthermore, the Soviets do not issue radiation meters to tell a soldier what dose he may have received. So, if a Russian tanker decides he's a zombie, he'll have no way to back up his decision. My guess is that he will turn his tank around and, as best he can, head toward possible medical attention, which might very well save his life.

placement unit to go like hell until it is knocked out. The name of the game of Soviet tank armies is blitzkrieg.

For Scoville and his fellow scientists to presume that they are better military experts than the professional military experts is, shall we say, rather presumptuous. Anybody has a right to play soldier. But the least he can do before he plays is to find out how real soldiers play. Even if the zombie diversion had some credibility to it, the logical thing to do would be to make sure that the would-be zombies would join the ranks of the immediately incapacitated. Throw in another neutron weapon. There's no law against it.

Actually there's a good deal of evidence indicating that zombies will be lousy tankers, no matter how heroically they may try to behave. Operating a tank is not the same as driving a Chevy with power steering, power brakes and everything else—with nobody shooting at you. It calls for closely coordinated action by the tank crew, some of whom must perform very precise functions if an enemy tank or antitank crew isn't to shoot them up. If the distress of radiation sickness, while not incapacitating, succeeds in reducing the performance of key tank operators, the whole act can go to pot and you're a sitting duck for the other side. However, these are detailed considerations that a curious reader can check up on if he wishes.

Finally, from a radiological standpoint, the zombie business is nothing more than an unfounded contrivance by people who really should know better (I suspect most of them do). We'd all be better off were the Scovilles to be a bit more curious and find out about the military facts of the situation before going off half-cocked.

CLAIM NUMBER 2: IT'S EASY TO SHIELD THE TANK CREW AGAINST NEUTRONS.

It is, providing you're willing to incapacitate the tank in order to prevent the tank crew from being incapacitated. If one wants to put shielding around the tank crew-compartment that is sufficient to reduce the effectiveness of a neutron bomb, one will have succeeded in piling so much weight on the tank that it simply won't be able to perform. It will be so hobbled by all this weight that it will be no match for enemy tanks or enemy antitank weapons.

For example, George Kistiakowsky, who twenty years later still is fighting the neutron bomb, writes in MIT's prestigious *Technology Review:* "A 10-cm (about 4 inches) layer of a suitable hydrogenous material, say, water in plastic bags over the crew compartment, followed by a thin sheet of cadmium metal, would reduce neutron radiation intensity by about a factor of 5. Thus, the effective range of an [N-bomb] would be reduced drastically." Kistiakowsky has been one of the great chemists of his time, but in reaching this conclusion he indicates that he is neither a great shielding expert nor an expert on how nuclear radiation propagates through air. Moreover, his naivete on the military factors surrounding armored operations is something to behold.

Shielding a tank crew against neutrons is an enormously complicated problem. It is not solved by simply placing the shield over the crew compartment. By the time the neutrons reach the tank, they are bouncing around in all directions, and to protect the crew properly, the shielding will have to be placed around the sides of the crew compartment as well. As a consequence, the shielding weight begins to pile up: to a much greater level than Kistiakowsky realizes. But even then, his claim that his shielding scheme will reduce the effective range of the N-bomb "drastically" doesn't hold water, no more than will his punctured plastic bags.

If one goes meticulously through the responsible calculations of how neutrons go through air, he will find that a reduction by a factor of five in the neutron intensity will result in a mere 15 to 20 percent reduction in the effective range of a one-kiloton N-bomb. This would mean that the range would drop from one thousand yards to perhaps eight hundred yards; hardly a "drastic" reduction. Truly large reductions in effective range—say 50 percent or more—would call for so much shielding weight that the tank driver and turret operator would have their abilities seriously reduced. The tank's mobility would be cut appreciably, as would the ability to swing the turret around to fire at acquired targets. In fact, were the tank to be shielded to a degree where the radiation was no longer the primary threat (i.e., it would take the blast itself to do in the tank, by knocking it off its treads, crushing vulnerable parts, etc.), the added weight would cripple the tank's combat effectiveness.

The U.S. Army has sponsored research into the tank-shielding problem for many years. Had the results of this research indicated that effective shielding was feasible and practical, would the army have dared try to hoodwink the President, the Congress, the Secretary of Defense and everybody else by putting in requirements for neutron warheads? Of course not! Surely this must have occurred to those scientific detractors. Or did it?

CLAIM NUMBER 3: N-BOMBS PRODUCE CANCER AND GENETIC ABERRATIONS.

Last summer I got a call from *Discover,* which heralds itself as the "Newsmagazine of Science." They were doing a piece on the neutron bomb and wanted to ask me some questions. This was fine with me. They queried away for a while in the military area. "Don't you have any technical questions you want to ask?" I said, adding that I had never seen even a reasonably accurate technical accounting of the N-bomb in the media. I was assured that this accounting would indeed be accurate; they were getting the data from official government sources. When the article came out, the media's batting average had not been improved.

"Beyond a mile and a quarter [for a one-kiloton neutron weapon], radiation would probably cause few deaths, but those exposed could face weeks of nausea, vomiting, loss of appetite, bloody diarrhea, loss of hair and skin disorders. The probability of their developing cancer later in life would be greatly increased, and their offspring, if any, would be marred by an increased incidence of birth defects," the article claimed—absolutely untruthfully. I doubt that the *Discover* reporters went through the official material. If they had done so, they couldn't possibly have reached such conclusions. That is, unless they had reached their conclusions beforehand.

For nearly thirty years the U.S. government, in an effort to keep the public fully informed on the dos and don'ts of nuclear weapons, has put out (from time to time, as more information was accrued) an official manual on the subject called "The Effects of Nuclear Weapons." I have in front of me the latest issue (1977), prepared and published by the Defense Department and the Energy Department. Let's see how they check off some of these distressing symptoms claimed by *Discover*.

At a distance of a mile and a quarter, my friend Jess calculates that there will be a radiation dose of ten rems. (The *rem* is the standard unit of dose used by radiobiologists in assessing the different effects of nuclear radiation.) Here's the official checklist for the dose range zero to a hundred rems:

Incidence of vomiting:	None
Characteristic signs*:	None below fifty rems
Prognosis:	Excellent
Convalescent period:	None
Incidence of death:	None

It's true that doses ranging from one hundred to a few hundred rems will result in definite radiation injury. There will probably be very few near-term deaths in this category. However, the evidence at hand indicates that there will be a marked increase in the incidence of long-term deaths, specifically those caused by cancer (especially leukemia) induced by these higher doses. This increase could be ten to thirty times greater than the rate occurring in unexposed personnel.† Since there will be large areas on the battlefield covered by these radiation doses, it has been claimed that there would be large numbers of cancer victims cropping up many years later.

However, the fact that there would be an increase in the number of people who would develop leukemia‡ later on as a result of exposure to neutron bomb radiation seems insignificant when one compares that number to the number of long-term deaths that would be traced to wounds suffered during a conventional war (recurring wound infections, intestinal malfunctions, lung damage, etc.). Long-term deaths resulting from those "conventional

* This includes the symptoms such as *Discover* lists: nausea, loss of appetite, bloody diarrhea, etc.

† As suggested by an analysis of the Hiroshima and Nagasaki experience.

‡ In 1980, according to figures provided by the Leukemia Society of America, Inc., the incidence of death caused by leukemia in the United States was roughly seven per hundred thousand. If this number were increased tenfold as a result of exposure to neutron bomb radiation, the incidence of death would be about seventy per hundred thousand.

wounds" far outnumber those that would result from neutron radiation-induced leukemia. (And if we consider the numbers of leukemia victims that would arise in the civilian ranks as a result of the radioactive fallout of the dirty, big-bang tactical weapons—which neutron bomb critics seem loathe to criticize, and which our European allies continue to accept for deployment on their territory—the number of enemy military victims hardly seems worth discussing.)

As to *Discover*'s claim of increased sterility and, even more horrifying, birth defects, unfortunately once again, we do not have sufficient data. But a few years ago, Britain's Professor Joseph Rotblat, a long-time opponent of nuclear weapons and an expert in this area, summarized the findings of a large body of scientific investigators who, for years, combed through data relating to the possible genetic damage in the offspring of Hiroshima and Nagasaki radiation victims (who obviously couldn't have been sterile). He said: "No genetic effects in children conceived [by atomic bomb victims] after the explosion have been found so far, despite a vigorous search."*

This result has been puzzling to scientists. It's not that the facts negate the theory. Rather, it's that the theorists do not yet understand the problem well enough to be able to make accurate predictions. But one thing is obvious, radiation survivors on the neutron battlefield will not sire a new race of genetic monsters.

CLAIM NUMBER 4: N-BOMB EXPLOSIONS MAKE THE AREA UNDERNEATH UNINHABITABLE FOR A LONG TIME.

Although, as explained earlier, the fusion reactions in a neutron weapon do not directly produce radioactivity (as is the case in a fission weapon), in certain soils the neutrons from N-bombs will be swallowed up by certain elements that then become radioactive. This production of what is called "induced activity" has induced a number of N-bomb opponents to claim that the weapon,

* Joseph Rotblat, "The Puzzle of Absent Effects," *New Scientist,* August 25, 1977.

because it maximizes the output of neutrons that cause this radioactivity, may actually be counterproductive militarily under certain circumstances, and dangerous to civilians who reside in the attacked area. For example, Stanford's Sidney Drell, a nuclear physicist and deputy director of Stanford's famed atom-smasher, which produces scads of induced activity, writes: "Although designed to increase the prompt neutron radiation that kills people but does not destroy buildings, they [N-bombs] can still extensively spread dirty radioactive debris that renders large areas uninhabitable for long periods of time." This is patently false.

Were neutron bombs to be burst close to the surface—i.e., at a height of several hundred feet—up to a distance of perhaps fifteen hundred to two thousand feet from ground zero, the radiation-dose rate (from the induced activity) would appear to be worrisome for friendly troops that would occupy the area after it is attacked. However, for this dose to be realistically worrisome, the troops would have to remain in the area for many hours, even days, before they accrued harmful levels of radiation. But we're talking about World War I here, not nuclear World War III, in which armored forces have to be almost continually on the go. If the friendly forces (our forces) insist on camping in the area they've attacked with a neutron bomb, they'll be setting themselves up for the kill by an enemy nuclear attack. That wouldn't make good military sense.

However, bursting neutron bombs several hundred feet above the ground is not the way to use the weapon. As explained here, in order to keep from destroying civilian buildings, it is necessary to burst much higher: say, twenty-five hundred to three thousand feet. If this is done, the radiation intensity from the induced activity drops drastically, by as much as twenty or thirty times. This is because there's now a much greater distance between the neutron source (the N-bomb) and the ground. It's like somebody with bad breath: If he's right next to you, you'll really know it; if he's across the room, you won't care.

With this higher burst the friendly troops can move into the attacked area as soon as they want, stay as long as they want and be safe. But for the military reason given above, they'd be fools if they did.

As for the civilians returning to their residential areas only to find that they can't stay there because of radioactive contamination, unless we want to destroy both their residences and contaminate the area they occupy, waving the induced activity red herring is to ignore what the neutron bomb is all about. By bursting the bomb high, the problem essentially disappears.

CLAIM NUMBER 5: OF ALL THE EFFECTS ON HUMANS FROM MILITARY WEAPONS, THE RADIATION EFFECTS FROM N-BOMBS ARE THE MOST INHUMANE IN HISTORY.

Those making this claim come from many varied walks of life. They are not just scientists and popular-science writers, although the latter two have hardly been quiet on this moral issue. Prominent in one walk of life, politics, is Senator H. John Heinz (R-Pa.), who stated on the Senate floor, when the Senate convened in a rare secret session to debate the neutron bomb: "Are we being asked here to approve a nuclear weapon that is even more repugnant than usual, which is literally dehumanizing? The neutron bomb, after all, singles out people for destruction, choosing to preserve buildings instead. Moreover, it works its effects by radiation rather than the more traditional emphasis on blast and heat."

In September 1981, I wrote a letter to the Secretary of Energy in Washington (at that time, our nuclear weapons development program was under his auspices), complaining about the government's refusal to go on record officially explaining what the neutron bomb was all about.

> September 10, 1981
>
> Honorable James B. Edwards
> Secretary of Energy
> Department of Energy
> Washington, D.C. 20585
>
> Dear Secretary Edwards:
>
> Last week, I was interviewed by a West German television company on the neutron bomb. In the course of the interview, I was asked a number of questions having to do

with the nature of nuclear radiation effects: What about the claims that the radiation would not put tank crews permanently out of action? What about the lingering radioactivity? What about the moral aspects of radiation effects—the "agonizing" deaths over weeks and months, the production of cancer and genetic abberations in both military personnel and west European civilians? Etc.

My answers and explanations of radiation effects startled my interviewer, who claimed that his countrymen and, in particular, his Chancellor never had been told these facts by the United States Government. He also mentioned that perhaps Helmut Schmidt's biggest personal hangup on the neutron bomb was over the "immoral" nature of nuclear radiation effects.

Why is it, Mr. Secretary, that after more than four years of intense, often acrimonious and almost always highly emotional, debate over the neutron bomb, the government has never put out an official statement to dispel the distorted technical charges which have been made about the weapon's effectiveness and alleged immorality? It seems to me that had this been done at the start, today we would not have the same anti-nuclear scientists making the same distorted charges; leaving the American people as confused as ever—and probably the Europeans as well.

I would strongly suggest that DOE and DOD get together (as they did some 30 years ago, when they first issued "The Effects of Nuclear Weapons" to responsibly inform the American people what nuclear weapons were all about) and provide an official document spelling out the true facts of the issue. Were such an effort mounted, in no way would it have to involve any classified material or the need to declassify any material. All of the relevant information long has been unclassified.

With best wishes.

Sincerely yours,

S. T. COHEN

STC/glw

I received a "fly-in-the-soup" letter in response.

Oct. 6, 1981

Department of Energy
Washington, D.C. 20545

Dear Mr. Cohen:

Secretary Edwards has asked me to reply to your recent correspondence in which you raised the issue of an official Government statement to refute distorted charges about the effectiveness and moral aspects of enhanced radiation warheads.

I was interested in reading the account of your recent interview by a West German television company on enhanced radiation warheads. I would appreciate it if you would send me a transcript of your replies to the questions you mentioned regarding the effects of nuclear radiation. I agree that a better public relations effort might have been made in preparation for announcement of a decision to produce enhanced radiation warheads. We have, however, always attempted to present to the news media the facts concerning these weapons in a completely forthright manner. What has subsequently come out in the press and on television, however, has not always been accurate or unbiased.

I am confident that the various departments within the executive branch of the Government concerned with enhanced radiation warheads now have a coordinated effort to present the true facts to the public. Secretary of Defense Weinberger, for example, held multiple press conferences on August 10, 1981, with the Independent News Network, ABC's Good Morning America, Cable News Network, West German television, and the Pentagon press corps to present official Government statements on enhanced radiation warheads. Secretary Weinberger also wrote an article for the Washington Post which appeared in the edition of August 11, 1981. In this article he clearly explained the Government's position concerning the capabilities of enhanced radiation warheads, and he also refuted popular misconceptions. The State Department has also prepared questions and answers on the subject for use by diplomats worldwide. We, at the Department of Energy, participated in the preparation of the information that has been used by both the Department of Defense and the State Department in their treatment of enhanced radiation warheads.

Your interest in providing the public with an objective analysis of enhanced radiation warheads is both understandable and appreciated. I assure you we shall continue to strive for this goal. The efforts of people like you in assisting in this endeavor whenever the opportunity arises is most helpful.

Sincerely,

WILLIAM W. HOOVER
Major General, USAF
Director of Military Application

I've found it most curious, indeed remarkable, that considering the tremendous, practically worldwide, flap that has been raised over the neutron bomb's radiation effects, the government has never moved to dispell many of the unfounded claims that have been made on the immorality of such a weapon. Without a doubt, the most vehement objections to the neutron bomb have been over the singularly inhumane nature of these effects. So if the government really wanted to produce and deploy the bomb, why didn't it conduct a factual defense of it to try and un-confuse millions of ordinary lay-people and maybe even straighten out some professionals, whose attacks on the Bomb were technically unwarranted? Or was the government afraid of getting into a hopeless fracas on such an emotional issue and thereby suffering a political disaster?

I'd guess that the decision to remain quiet on this issue was based on the wisdom that political discretion was more advisable than factual valor. If so, this was hardly the first time the government acted in this fashion.

Lacking the wisdom of our political leaders, I've never hesitated to rush into this extremely sensitive subject (of nuclear radiation) and give my own opinion and judgment. This was because I fiercely believed in neutron bombs and thought they offered the best prospects for the morally defensible use of nuclear weapons. And I'll rush in again here—not to try and turn you into a believer like me, but rather to discuss the radiation issue in a factual framework. And there *are* a few facts that bear on the issue.

Before we start assessing the relevance and validity of Claim Number 5 (a condemnation of a weapon whose effectiveness stems from the massive irradiation of human beings), we should place the issue in its proper context. The human beings at issue here are soldiers. From our standpoint, they are *enemy* soldiers. And they are intent on conquering our allies. Their leaders have certainly shown no qualms about using any kind of weapon to facilitate such conquest. Should we go to war to defend our allies, the basic purpose of our soldiers will be to kill the enemy soldiers. In a world that has always been hell-bent on fighting wars, that's what war has always been about.

To serve this purpose, our soldiers will use bullets that can tear up a person's insides, antitank weapons that shower enemy tank crews with high-velocity fragments, concussion weapons (euphemistically referred to as fuel-air explosives) that collapse lungs and rupture vital organs, napalm that burns a human body beyond recognition, land mines that blow off limbs, high-velocity rifle ammunition that mutilates its victims, and so on. If the President is willing to release neutron bombs, our soldiers will use these weapons too. All this for the express purpose of killing. The addition of neutron weapons to our arsenal will not change this situation.

Besides being able to kill (in fact, having been *created* to kill), all these weapons, conventional and nuclear, are capable of injuring military personnel. The general experience in conventional war has been that for every soldier killed, a larger number have been wounded to one degree or another.* During the Great Patriotic War against the Germans in World War II, the Red Army suffered the staggering total of about fourteen million soldiers wounded. Of this horrendous total, well over a million (we don't have precise numbers) wound up permanently disabled—blind, crippled, vital organs impaired, etc., which is a terrible toll in human mutilation for others to contemplate, and for the mutilated to contemplate, as long as they lived after the war.

The Russian casualties of the last war are brought up here because the Red Army is regarded by the United States as the

* In World War II the Japanese Imperial Army experienced just about the opposite ratio; which says a great deal about how the generals regarded the lives of their soldiers.

prime, even sole, target for U.S. neutron bombs in the next war, if it comes to that. Were this war to take place using only conventional weapons, there is no way to predict how many killed and injured (with some fraction permanently disabled) the Red Army might suffer. But unless NATO throws in the towel very quickly after a conflict has started (a distinct possibility unless there is a drastic beefing up of its conventional forces), when the war is over, very large numbers of Russian soldiers, maybe hundreds of thousands, will wind up on the disabled list: mutilated by the effects of conventional weapons that nations, including the United States, have accepted as the price of going to war.

Were neutron weapons used against enemy personnel, what would the nature of the human disablement be after the war? In what condition would those who had been "wounded" by nuclear radiation be? Would the all-too-familiar scene of widespread human mutilation on the streets and in the veterans hospitals present itself?

As a first example of what happens to those who are "wounded" by nuclear radiation on the field of battle, consider the fate of those exposed to high, but nonlethal, doses of radiation during the atomic bomb attacks against Hiroshima and Nagasaki. The official U.S. government publication "The Effects of Nuclear Weapons" makes the following observation on Japanese radiation casualties:

> Those patients in Japan who survived for three to four months, and did not succumb to tuberculosis, lung diseases or other complications,* gradually recovered. There was no evidence of permanent loss of hair, and examination of 824 survivors some 3 to 4 years later showed that their blood composition was not significantly different from that of a control group in a city not subjected to nuclear attack.

Over the years there have been a number of radiation accidents where people have been exposed to doses sufficiently high to cause radiation sickness, but not death. To be sure, the distress

* These complications are not uniquely attributable to radiation. Rather, they developed as a result of the overall trauma of being subjected to the atomic bomb attack, which lowered resistance to infectious diseases, and the conditions that existed after the attack.

suffered by these people was great indeed. Specific symptoms included vomiting, diarrhea, dizziness, chills, fever, and so on. These symptoms have been played up by those who oppose N-bombs as being particularly insidious, reflecting terrible agony on the part of the victims. How agonizing are these symptoms? This has to be a purely personal, subjective judgment, each of us having different pain thresholds and different interpretations of the misery we go through when we get sick.

I remember my dad refusing to go to bed when he would come down with any sickness that causes vomiting, diarrhea, chills, fever, and the like. He chose to go stoicly about his trade—carpentry. On the other hand, when my wife comes down with some brand of influenza that produces some of these symptoms, to watch her and listen to her, you'd think she was about to join her ancestors. On far more than one occasion, when I've overindulged in some alcoholic concoction, I've almost wished I could do the same.

With this as a backdrop, let's take a look at two clinical accounts of radiation sickness produced by very high radiation exposures that, on a statistical basis, held respectable probabilities of death. These two cases are fairly representative of what might result from exposure to a neutron bomb burst. They are also fairly representative of the response of victims of radiation accidents, who received similar exposures:

> (Upon admission to the hospital—an hour after exposure) the patient (who had experienced about 400 rads) was in good physical condition . . . The patient was calm and had no subjective complaints. . . . Although he felt well on admission to the hospital, the patient vomited once several hours later. In the course of the next twelve hours the nausea disappeared and the patient's appetite returned. There was no diarrhea, or other gastrointestinal disturbance . . . For several days after exposure the patient felt weak and tired and appeared prostrated but was otherwise asymptomatic. . . . The patient's strength improved steadily, and he suffered no untoward reaction to being allowed out of bed several hours a day after the tenth day. . . . On the fifteenth day the patient was discharged from the hospital. . . . Approximately ten weeks after exposure, the patient's strength

> and endurance were back to normal and he returned to work. Since this time he has led an entirely normal life, working hard and engaging in outdoor sports.
>
> * * * *
>
> In June 1974 a radiation worker at an industrial plant in New Jersey accidentally received a whole body dose of approximately 600 rads (450 rad average bone-marrow dose) from a cobalt-60 (gamma) source. The victim exhibited prodromal symptoms (specifically nausea and vomiting) of acute radiation sickness, commencing some thirty to sixty minutes postexposure. During the two and a half to three hours that elapsed between the exposure and the victim's arrival at the hospital emergency room, he experienced ten episodes of vomiting. He was described as being concerned, but not unduly anxious, about his condition (it was further stated that he was the calmest individual in the hospital emergency room). In the days following his admission to the hospital, his white blood cell and platelet counts steadily decreased. During the twenty-second to thirty-fifth days postexposure, his blood count had dropped so low that only the large numbers of transfused platelets and granulocytes maintained his life. After the thirty-fifth day his condition improved rapidly; he was discharged from the hospital on the forty-fifth day and subsequently returned to full-time work.

On a statistical basis, the first victim described above had about a 50 percent chance of dying from his exposure of four hundred rads (a rad unit of dose is essentially the same as a rem unit). The second victim had about a 90 percent chance of dying. Both were lucky, because of their personal physiological makeup, and they lived. Obviously both went through considerable distress. As to how you and I might have reacted to such symptoms, you and I must figure that out for ourselves.

Speaking for myself, if I were going to be wounded on the field of battle, I'd far rather be dosed by radiation than burned by napalm, or crushed by blast concussion, or have my body torn up by a land mine or a fragmentation bomb. I'd also far rather just be irradiated by an N-bomb than irradiated, burned, crushed and thrown around (by the blast wind, which can reach velocities of hundreds of miles per hour) by an A-bomb. Far more important, as far as I'm personally concerned, I'd sure be willing to take my chances on leukemia showing up at some latter stage of my life, due to radiation, than be maimed and disabled by conventional weapons or A-bombs.

Note that both these victims were back to normal some number of weeks after their accidents. They bore no scars from their mishaps (apparently not even emotional scars) and were able to pick up where they left off when they were irradiated. As to how these aftermaths compare with those resulting from being wounded by conventional weapons, if one so desires you can find out by visiting the nearest Veterans Administration hospital.

But what about those soldiers who receive significantly higher doses of radiation and are doomed to die? Since the higher the dose the more severe these symptoms will be, what can we say about those victims who live for a few days or a few weeks? If we stick with what facts we have on this matter, all that can be said is that the trauma will be greater than for the nonlethal situation but that no uniquely different symptoms will appear. The larger the dose, the more severe the symptoms will be (and they will be terrible indeed) and the sooner the victim will die. If the dose is high enough, chances are the victim will die from shock almost immediately.

I have no intention here of trying to assess this "agonizing death" situation. There is no conceivable way of making a responsible judgment on whether a radiation victim dies more painfully than a victim of conventional weapons or of the blast and heat effects of fission tactical weapons. This is purely subjective. However, it has not stopped those who oppose neutron bombs from making such judgments, allegedly based on objective scientific data.

A couple of years ago I was invited to give a talk at the University of Missouri. The topic I chose to talk about was the survival of the United States in the Nuclear Age. The neutron bomb being especially controversial on most college campuses, I didn't even want to bring it up. And I didn't. But that didn't stop one of the students from bringing it up—but good.

This one young man arose, brandishing a piece of paper, and literally shrieked at me: "How could you ever devise such a fiendish weapon? Look at what it does to people!" And he recited what was apparently printed on the paper. It sounded very familiar and I asked him whether he was citing an article that had been written by a Stanford University scientist, and which was getting a lot of attention around the country. It was. So I gave him my opinion of that article.

I had read it in the *Los Angeles Times* (November 11, 1981). It was entitled "Neutron Weapons: an Agonizing Death (I've seen it)" by J. Garrott Allen, billed as a professor emeritus of surgery at Stanford University Medical School, a founding member of the Radiation Research Society and author of numerous articles on the effects of radiation injury. Pretty darned good credentials. Professor Allen had been at Los Alamos in May 1946, as a physician, when a radiation accident occurred and one of the scientists, Louis Slotin, received a high, supralethal dose of radiation, mostly neutrons. Allen was one of the attending physicians to Slotin. His article gave a vividly horrifying account of the suffering Slotin went through (emphasizing the terrible burns on his hands and arms) before he died nine days later. (He probably would have died a lot sooner had he not been given prompt and continual medical attention, which would be the case for soldiers on the nuclear battlefield.)

In summing up, Professor Allen stated that those who die from nuclear radiation effects on the battlefield will suffer deaths "almost as agonizing to those looking on as to the victims themselves. The production of neutron weapons is probably as immoral a concept as human minds have yet devised." I do not choose to comment on how agonizing a neutron bomb death might be. But I will say that the agony Louis Slotin went through did not "duplicate what would happen to a person exposed to a [neutron weapon]."

At the time of the accident Slotin was standing right over a ball of plutonium that released a flood of neutrons as the result of a chain reaction. His hands were the part of his body closest to the ball (as Allen faithfully reported), so they were terribly burned by the almost unbelievably high neutron intensity. Next closest were his arms and, as described in Allen's article, they too were badly burned. But this is not what would result from exposure to a neutron bomb, and Allen must surely understand this. Lethal neutron bomb exposure occurs many hundreds of yards from the burst, where radiation intensities of the magnitude that caused the terrible burns to Slotin simply cannot exist. (Allen never mentioned the terrible burns that can result from flame thrower or napalm attacks—or, for that matter, as a result of the heat from fission battlefield nuclear weapons.)

Those who choose to put an "inhumane" label on neutron weapons are, of course, free to do so. In an absolute sense, they're correct. But then, this goes for practically any weapon. That's what military weapons are all about. They symbolize man's inhumanity to man. However, I would opine that if those morally opposed to the N-bomb are going to be truly objective, while they decry the inhumaneness of neutron bombs, they ought to compare their inhumaneness with that of other weapons. But they won't. That's bad politics.

CHAPTER 6
DO THE RUSSIANS HAVE THE N-BOMB?

"MANY YEARS AGO . . . WE TESTED that bomb. We tested, but we never started production of that weapon." This was the claim Leonid Brezhnev made to a group of U.S. senators visiting in Moscow. Once Big Brother had let out the word in November 1978, the acolytes joined in. Soviet intelligence officers would tell their U.S. counterparts the same tale, but to oblige their curious American colleagues, they were more specific about when: ten years ago.

How much of this was true? And if it was true, why did the Russians decide to let the cat out of the bag? In disclosing the news of the neutron bomb tests, Brezhnev went so far as to give the name of the Soviet scientist in charge of the tests, a guy by the name of Korolyov. The Russians are no idiots when it comes to informing and disinforming the West. They know that our intelligence can at least check on people. Once Korolyov had been shoved into neutron show biz by his president, they must have known that our supersleuths would run him through their data processing and find out whether or not he was a real live nuclear weapons scientist.

Not having had access to these data banks and whatever use the sleuths may have made of them, I feel free to guess that they checked up on Brezhnev's claim and found out his claim was right. Korolyov had indeed worked on nukes. (Putting on my Boy Scout hat, I can't believe that had our sleuths determined that Brezhnev was lying through his teeth, the lie wouldn't have gotten out to the American people, or at least to the American senators to whom Brezhnev gave the scoop. If you can't trust Brezhnev, that's one thing. And if you can't trust the CIA, well—whom can you trust? Lastly, if you can't trust an American senator to tell the American people whether or not the Soviet president had lied to him, well . . .)

There is more to the Soviet claim.

Shortly after my neutron bomb sales campaign had started, I became aware of a paper presented at Geneva in 1957 by the Soviet nuclear physicist L. A. Artsimovich. He had played a key role in Russia's development of the hydrogen bomb, and it had brought him official gratitude from his government. Artsimovich was reporting on Soviet research on nuclear explosives directed for peaceful application to the Second United Nations' International Conference on the Peaceful Uses of Atomic Energy.

In his report he described a series of experiments conducted by the Soviets that utilized "pure-fusion" explosive devices for nonmilitary application, such experiments having begun in 1952. This was well before the United States embarked on such a program. In effect, what he also reported on, should this peaceful pursuit have been directed to military purposes, was the "ultimate" neutron bomb; i.e., a weapon that worked without benefit of a fission trigger. Such a neutron bomb would produce no significant amounts of the long-lived dangerous radioactivity that fission reactions produce. Moreover, in contrast to a fission-fusion neutron weapon, it would put the maximum emphasis on producing neutrons, to incapacitate enemy soldiers, and the maximum deemphasis on blast and heat effects that might knock down and incinerate civil property. For those who like neutron bombs, this would be the dreamboat version.

Let's get a little technical: Artsimovich was talking to a highly qualified group of nuclear experts. Here's what he reported:

> A pulsed thermonuclear reaction may also be possible under conditions when a high temperature is reached during the compression and implosion produced . . . by a charge of conventional explosives (such as TNT, or something more powerful) surrounding a capsule of deuterium or a mixture of deuterium and tritium. Without going into details of the experiments, it should be mentioned that the conditions have been found under which the generation of *neutrons* [emphasis added] both in the D+T and the D+D reactions is detected with absolute reliability and reproducibility. In experiments conducted in 1952, it was possible to record both fast neutrons that passed through the charge without any great loss of energy as well as neutrons that were slowed down in the explosive.

Just exactly how successful these experiments may have been, we may never know. There was no further reporting by the Russians after this statement was issued. However, that Artsimovich and Co. were pursuing a theoretically feasible approach, there is no doubt. If the Russians actually succeeded in this project, they have an enormous lead in neutron bomb technology over the United States, since the technology of the warheads now going into our stockpile requires a fission trigger. Were the tests mentioned by Brezhnev of the pure-fusion variety? Again, we may never know. All we do know is that activity highly relevant to neutron bomb development started a very long time ago in the USSR.

Later, in September 1961, in the Soviet military journal *Red Star,* an article by Colonel M. Pavlov appeared, entitled "On Plans for the Neutron Bomb." The article was apparently stimulated by the debate going on in the United States and Senator

Dodd's arguments for pure-fusion neutron weapons. On this basis, one would have expected that Colonel Pavlov, loyal to his Kremlin masters, would have put forth a distorted propaganda blast showing, as had Khrushchev and the rest of the Soviet propaganda apparatus, that the weapon was a mass exterminator of people. To the contrary, and I might say this has been a fairly consistent feature of Soviet military writing, he gave an accurate and dispassionate technical accounting of how the pure-fusion neutron bomb would work, and what it would do.

What Colonel Pavlov described was a weapon that would have been the logical product of Artsimovich's project, provided it turned out successfully. The weapon was based on the fusion of deuterium and tritium. According to Pavlov's calculations, its radiation effects could reach out as far as five hundred yards to neutralize personnel, without destroying property. (One can hardly associate this radius of effects with a weapon that will wipe out entire populations as Soviet propaganda then was claiming—and has continued to claim.*) Pavlov concluded his technical discussion by properly describing what the neutron bomb is:

* Writing to President Jimmy Carter in January 1978, Leonid Brezhnev claimed: "By their very nature and their destructive characteristics, neutron weapons can strike not only people wearing military uniforms, but also huge masses of the population. These are inhuman weapons of mass destruction; they are directed against people. . . . The reality is that if neutron weapons are ever used, a devastating scythe will sweep across the territories of entire countries, probably not leaving a single inch untouched."

> . . . it is obvious that the neutron bomb is a variety of nuclear bombs in which the energy of the blast is redistributed between [military] strike factors in favor of the flow of neutrons. Under specific blast conditions, the main strike factors will not be the light emission [heat] or shock wave, but the penetrating radiation, the basic force of which will consist of neutrons.

So one notes that some three decades back, the Soviets began a nuclear explosive program that had the earmarks of a darned good neutron bomb (as good as can be made), and some two decades ago showed a full understanding of the basic principle of the neutron bomb.

I might digress here and say that on more than one occasion I've tweaked my intellectual vanity by wondering whether or not I really was the first guy to discover the neutron bomb principle. Considering how technically simple and straightforward the basic concept is, I have told myself that somewhere, sometime, someone else must have thought it up. But who? Since in the United States there had been no real incentive for anyone to devise the idea, unless he was a maverick like myself who had beliefs contrary to the nuclear party line, it was easy for me to rationalize full credit for myself. But the Russian party line on nuclear weapons has never conformed to ours. For very sound military reasons, and motivated rather than inhibited by the party line, a Soviet nuclear weapons analyst such as Pavlov could easily have invented and proposed the idea years before I did.

Eleven years after Colonel Pavlov's article was published, two Soviet armored warfare experts, General Biryukov and Colonel Melnikov, wrote a book, *Antitank Warfare,* in which the advantage of nuclear radiation as a "tank killer" was discussed. Their claims just happened to agree with those of high-ranking U.S. government officials, including two Presidents: Neutrons are really the cat's pajamas for knocking out enemy armored forces. (Yet these U.S. government officials, including two Presidents, have been telling the Soviets that the Russians have no use for neutron weapons.) On the advantages of using nuclear radiation, and thus neutron bombs, against armored forces, the Soviet authors wrote:

> . . . in performing the mission of destroying armored troops on the field of battle, it is expedient to destroy such a basic

> element as the tank crews in and outside the tanks. This makes it possible to deprive the enemy armored troops of their combat power with a greater economy of ammunition, in shorter periods, and with a high destructive probability.

If Soviet military experts found it more effective to knock out tank crews with radiation than to knock out tanks with blast, thereby giving full emphasis to establishing neutron weapons requirements, would they have other good reasons for emphasizing such requirements? They sure would, because of their highly offensive military doctrine for their armored forces, and despite U.S. claims that neutron weapons are strictly for defensive purposes.

When the French planned their Maginot Line, one of the reasons why they did not extend it along the Belgian border was that their military experts decided that the German tanks would not be able to move easily through the Ardennes Forest. The forest itself was believed to be an effective barrier against the German blitzkrieg tactics. And it was judged that French forces could be moved into the area, if need be, to prevent penetration into France. Of course, the French experts proved to be terribly wrong. The German tanks traversed the forest like a razor going through Camembert cheese. The Maginot Line was outflanked, and that was the end of France.

Had a series of tornadoes swept through the Ardennes Forest just prior to the German attack, it is very possible that France might have been spared from invasion. Had this happened, the vaunted Panzer forces would have come across many areas where there was extensive tree blowdown, posing a tremendous problem for traversal. Nature would have blitzed the blitzkrieg. In fact, had the Allied forces in France in 1940 had the capability to lay down a sufficient artillery barrage in front of the advancing German armor, they might have succeeded in knocking down a sufficient number of trees to impede the advance. This artillery employment was a standard defensive tactic in World War II. It still is.

Had the French possessed a hundred or so atomic bombs for such employment, in effect they would have possessed a hundred or so nuclear tornadoes. When the shock wave of an atomic bomb sweeps by, its immediate aftermath is an unbelievably high wind that can reach velocities of hundreds of miles per hour. In a forested area these winds will blow down trees as if they were matchsticks. A Hiroshima-size atomic bomb can cause such blowdown over a diameter of a few miles. Such blowdown would produce huge problems for any armored force trying to move through the area. Soviet military strategists know this full well. They have expressed great concern over the possibility of tactical nuclear weapons producing such obstacles. Curiously this concern focuses on the use of *our* weapons, not their weapons. This can be translated to mean either that they are not about to inform their tank force commanders that *their* weapons may also be the culprits for producing such inhibiting devastation, or that *their* weapons are not the same as ours, like maybe the weapons they burst in such areas are neutron weapons.

The same Soviet concern exists for nuclear attacks in urban areas. ("Under the conditions prevailing in a city, employment of nuclear weapons is limited inasmuch as they entail extensive destruction, piled rubble and regions which are almost impassible not only for the enemy but for friendly troops," wrote three senior Red Army strategists in 1971.) The apprehension over large areas of conflagration and radioactive contamination, which could be caused by tactical nuclear fission weapons, also shows up in Soviet strategic writings. But were neutron weapons being regarded in this context, there would be no valid reason for such apprehension.

We note then that not only would neutron weapons make good military sense for the Red Army in a direct sense, they also would make good sense indirectly, in that Russian armored forces could quickly move in to mop up in the attacked area, were the attack to be made with N-bombs. Again speaking candidly and technically accurately, as Soviet military writers usually do, in December of 1978 the chief of Soviet armored forces, Marshal Pavel Rotmistrov, readily acknowledged this feature of neutron bombs in an interview. He said: "Because the destructive effect of neutron bombs is relatively low, tankers [guys who operate tanks] will be able to accomplish combat missions in the zone of application of neutron bombs continuously and to the mission's limit of advance."

The marshal, during his interview, had a few uncharitable words for the Western imperialists regarding their contention that neutron bombs were intended solely for NATO use against a Warsaw Pact tank attack: "It is nothing but an attempt to make black look white when they declare neutron bombs a defensive weapon against advancing Soviet tanks. Surely they must be aware of the repeated statements by Soviet leaders that the joint armed forces of the Warsaw Pact are not going to make any tank rush to the Atlantic coast." Sure, Marshal, we're all aware of your country's repeated statements. But at the same time NATO doesn't trust you guys as far as it can throw the Iron Curtain. So just to play it safe, NATO has put almost a million men under arms and spends two or three hundred billion dollars a year trying to dissuade you guys from having a change of heart.

Suppose that one day the Soviets did have a change of heart, and did set forth for the Atlantic coast. If so, how much would they care about destroying the Continent in the process of conquering and occupying it? I think they would care a lot.

If one takes a good hard look at NATO military doctrine, and then at the Soviet doctrine (which is based in no small way on trying to understand ours, though unfortunately, the reverse has hardly been the case), one gets the idea that should the Soviets ever attack NATO Europe, they would attack the United States at the same time. Why? Because NATO's doctrine says that if the Red Army cannot be kept from overrunning Europe, the United States, in a magnificently self-sacrificial mood, will conduct strategic nuclear attacks on the Soviet Union. So the military logic of the Soviets would be to hit us before we hit them, thereby minimizing whatever damage we might do to them.

However, whatever this level of U.S.-produced damage in the Soviet Union might be, one thing is for sure: There will be one terrible amount of damage. If our remaining forces carried out attacks against Russian cities, as all U.S. Presidents have threatened, indeed pledged, to do, the devastation of the Soviet urban-industrial fabric would be something awful. Surely the Soviet planners, in contemplating going to war with the West, must have been taking this potential damage to their economic framework into account. They must have been seeking ways and means to ameliorate the magnitude of the disaster. And it is bound to be a disaster.

One possible solution to this problem would be to repeat what they did to the Eastern European countries they conquered and occupied after World War II. This would be to loot Western Europe of whatever key industrial facilities could be shipped to the USSR and put into operation (requiring the looting of key industrial personnel as well). Another possible solution would be to turn Western Europe into a slave labor camp and force industrial production to continue at gunpoint for the benefit of the USSR. For either solution to have any credibility, however, Western Europe would have to be reasonably intact after the war. If it weren't intact, the required industrial production would not exist. So, for their own selfish reasons, the Soviet Marxist-Leninist atheistic leaders, in conducting nuclear attacks on NATO Europe, would do well to show some Christianlike charity toward their Christian imperialist enemies.

There have been strong indications over the years by Soviet strategists that should there be a nuclear war with NATO, it would be desirable to constrain as much as possible the extent of economic damage. One rationale behind this desire was explained long ago in the official Soviet military journal *Military Thought* (November 1966):

> The objective is not to turn the large economic and industrial regions into a heap of ruins . . . but to deliver strikes which will destroy strategic combat means, paralyze enemy military production, making it incapable of satisfying the priority needs of the front and rear areas and sharply reduce the enemy capability to conduct strikes.

Just exactly how the Soviets might go about accomplishing this objective is up for grabs. Were I in charge of Soviet nuclear weapons requirements, and were I seeking a means to "paralyze enemy military production" where the political objective "is not to turn the large economic and industrial regions into a heap of ruins," I sure would give serious consideration to a neutron bomb solution. Having such a capability, all that would be required would be to get the word off to the downtrodden workers in NATO countries that if they work on military production, they will be neutron-bombed at their factories. If they stay home, no bombing. In either case, the production could be paralyzed without destroying the facilities.

Another rationale behind the desire to constrain economic damage is explained by this Soviet statement (which appeared in *Military Thought,* February 1969):

> Theses of Soviet military strategy primarily reflect the political strategy of the Communist Party of the Soviet Union. It is in the interests of political strategy that military strategy makes use of the achievements of scientific-technical progress which materialize in weapons of varying power. Some of these weapons are capable of doing considerable damage to a continent, others only to individual states . . . Finally, still others lead to defeat of the enemy's armed forces without doing essential injury to the economy or populace of states whose aggressive rulers unleashed the war . . .

Once more we see considerations of political objectives that, in turn, create logical considerations for neutron weapons. Neutron bombs would be admirably equipped to bring about the "defeat of the enemy's armed forces without doing essential injury to the economy or populace of states."

From statements such as the above, we get further evidence that the Soviet military does not feel itself bound to develop their weapons in accordance with the propaganda blasts issued by their political leaders against the weapon developments of the capitalists. These Communist statements are capitalistic as all get-out in their desire to preserve economic assets.

Do the Russians have the N-bomb? In terms of hard intelligence, we don't know. Short of actually stealing a Soviet nuclear warhead, analyzing it and concluding that it was indeed a neutron device, there is no way to make a foolproof determination. We lost the opportunity to make even crude guesses of Soviet warhead technology almost twenty years ago, when the Atmospheric Test Ban Treaty was signed. Even had the Soviets violated the treaty in order to test neutron warheads in the atmosphere (to determine more realistically the nature of their effects), because of their very low explosive power and low output of radioactivity (essentially none if they were testing pure-fusion neutron bombs), they could have pulled off such tests with little chance of detection by national verification means. (Some have argued, including myself, that the mystery nuclear explosion off the coast of South Africa in the fall of 1979 was a French effort to evade detection of a neutron bomb test.) In fact, quoting an official Pentagon statement made some years ago: "We do not know what the Soviets have accomplished in their test program since 1963."

On the other hand, if the smoking gun is missing from the nuclear detective story related here, there is an awful lot of circumstantial evidence to indicate that (a) the Soviets initiated research on nuclear devices with splendid neutron bomb properties long ago; (b) they have certainly understood the basic principles of the weapon for a long time; and (c) their military and political objectives in a major ground war would be well served by the employment of such weapons.

Alain Enthoven, the former Defense Department official during the McNamara regime under whose guidance the study that administered the *coup de grace* to the neutron bomb was made, once stated: "Rather than building large numbers of short-range, low-yield systems . . . the Soviets have emphasized higher-yield, mobile tactical missiles, primarily useful for terrain or blanketing fires. Indeed, the Soviet force structure raises serious doubts about their capability to fight a limited tactical nuclear war, much less one in which collateral damage and civilian casualties are to be kept to low levels." It was one thing for Enthoven to have effectively throttled Defense Department prospects for stockpiling highly discriminate tactical nuclear weapons. And it was quite another thing for him to claim that the Soviets had no more use for such weapons than he thought we should have. Let me explain how the Pentagon was able to do this when Enthoven was at the helm.

In 1969, just after Enthoven left the Pentagon, I was working there as a consultant, directing a tactical nuclear weapons study authorized by President Nixon. One of the key inputs to the study was, of course, the nature of the enemy's tactical nuclear stockpile—i.e., the Soviet stockpile. In this connection I arranged for a briefing by an intelligence officer whose responsibilities included this area.

The officer went through his song-and-dance act, telling me essentially what Enthoven said in the above statement. I asked him whether this assessment was based on hard evidence, thereby giving him the chance to get off the hook by pulling the classical stunt of the intelligence community: "Look, Mr. Cohen, we're talking here about the most sensitive level of intelligence, for which you don't have the tickets. I'd sure like to tell you why we feel this way, but you realize that I just can't. You'll have to take my word for it." However, this fellow was an honest man and told me that there was no hard evidence. What they had done was a Soviet requirements study, supposedly based on Soviet military strategy, which determined analytically what tactical nuclear stockpile the Soviets would logically want to develop. I then asked him to tell me about the study. And what I heard was just about what Enthoven's Colonel C. had told me several years earlier in explaining why *we* had no use for neutron bombs. It was the old "mirror imaging" game: "We have met the enemy and they are us."

The poor intelligence officer was embarrassed no end to have to tell me this. But that's the way it was. The Nixon administration policies on tactical nuclear weapons remained exactly what they had been during the Kennedy-Johnson years. And that's why nothing was done about the neutron bomb until the Congress decided that it had had enough of this attitude and forced the Pentagon to go for the Bomb.

Do the Russians have the neutron bomb? Why shouldn't they?

CHAPTER 7
THE MORALITY OF THE NEUTRON BOMB

WHEN THE SECOND NEUTRON BOMB debate broke out in the summer of 1977, I decided that I wasn't going to repeat my earlier folly and try to influence Washington. It wouldn't have done much good anyway. Those in favor of producing the Bomb didn't want my kind of help. All I could do was to provide constructive criticism on their nuclear weapons policies and try to keep them factual. They were interested in neither. So I decided to go public.

(Recall that in round one, as far as one Sam Cohen and the neutron bomb were concerned, the government regarded this as SECRET. If I had attempted to discuss the neutron bomb openly, as I have here, they would have cut me off at the knees. They would quite possibly have pressed security violation charges against me. Unless I had been a congressman.)

I went public by writing an article on the N-bomb that was accepted by the *Washington Star,* and all of a sudden, I was in show business, going through the terror of facing TV cameras, having magazine people come to my house to interview me and take pictures (my wife going through the horror of having to display a clean house for the photographers). If Washington was not interested in my views on the Bomb, practically everyone else was. I was even invited to a hippie church in Los Angeles, to hear a sermon and a chorale on the Bomb. I declined.

My wife and I became more socially acceptable than we ever dreamed was possible. Among other invitations, we received a dinner invitation from my friend Milt, a Beverly Hills millionaire (i.e., an ordinary Beverly Hills citizen) and a member in good standing of the Beverly Hills Jewish community (i.e., liberal Democrats with a tremendous concern for the well-being of Israel, and inclined to be opposed to nuclear bombs and power stations). We showed up at Milt's, along with a couple of dozen of his "Community" friends, many of whom I had met before and had discovered that their views on politics, war and peace, and nuclear weapons were not very congenial with mine.

After dinner Milt, beaming with pride, interrupted the standard "Community" chatter and said that he was sure that Sam was willing to answer any and all questions on the N-bomb. I was. The questioning started and it was far from friendly—naturally. At one point there came the inevitable question: Would it be good for Israel? "It sure would!" I exclaimed. And I proceeded to explain how Israel could conduct a really credible defense against hostile neighbors. With that, I noticed a change in the attitude of some of the guests.

The questioning went on until one of them asked me what my position on the Bomb was. I might as well have been asked if I loved my kids. So I decided to turn the question around. "Look," I said, "if I come out for the Bomb, you'll say that I'm letting my paternal bias show. If I come out against it, you'll say that I'm trying to be cute. So I'm not about to answer. Let's put the shoe on the other foot. How do you guys feel about it? Let's take a vote around the table." I conducted the poll and, by gosh, the Bomb won—by one vote. I was flabbergasted.

In the spring of 1978, my notoriety still high, I received a call from my old and dear friend Dick Cella, a retired air force general and a Manhattan restaurateur, asking me to come to New York to have dinner at his restaurant with a bunch of Italian friends of his he thought it was important for me to meet. Because of my friendship with Dick, and my passion for his restaurant, I accepted. In fact, even if Joe Schmo had invited me to have dinner at Dick's restaurant, I probably would have accepted.

I showed up at Dick's apartment for cocktails and met the Italians. Two of them were priests, but of what rank, I didn't know. Dick introduced me as an old friend from his air force days and I chatted amicably with a few of them, learning that the priests were monsignors, one of them a guy by the name of Giovanni Cheli (pronounced Kelly), who was the Vatican's observer to the United Nations.

After cocktails, we headed off for Dick's place, where we dined happily. The meal over, Dick shouted above the din (all in Italian, although almost all of them were fluent in English) that he wanted to say something. The something was that just in case anyone didn't know, Sam Cohen was the Father of the Neutron Bomb. He was certain that everyone had questions they wanted to ask, and he was also sure that I'd be willing to answer their questions.

The questioning started. Most of the guests seemed sympathetic to the idea of the neutron bomb. But not the two priests, who asked most of the questions, which were more in the form of assertions against the Bomb, from a moral standpoint—of course. The priests hammered away and I responded as best I could, not being used to interrogation by men of the cloth. We really went at it, hot and heavy.

Finally the same question was asked as during the Beverly Hills affair: Do you favor producing the Bomb? My answer was the same: Let's see how you vote. I started with the person who asked the question, who was seated directly to the left of the priests, and went clockwise around the table. At least this cross-section of Italians, who seemed decidedly conservative, really seemed to like the Bomb. The Bomb batted about .900 until I hit the priests, the first one being Monsignor Cheli. The monsignor voted aye and I thought Cella was going to have a coronary. So did the second one.

The vote over, the discussion shifted to other matters, and some time later, Cella came over to me and asked me to accompany him to his office. When we got there, he closed the door, looked at me and said: "Sam, you have just made the most important conversion of your life. Before you met Cheli, he was dead set against the neutron bomb. And now, after listening to your arguments, he's for it. This is just the beginning. You're going to hear more about this." He proved to be dead right.

A few weeks later Cella, who had obviously conferred with Cheli, called me. Would I be willing to come back to New York for another dinner, this time to be held at the Vatican Mission, and to dine with Archbishop Agostino Casaroli, who was coming into town to address the United Nations Disarmament Conference. Casaroli, Dick explained, was, in effect, the Vatican's foreign minister, and also Cheli's boss.

Back I came. Dick and I showed up at the mission and were escorted to the dining room where a dozen or so people waited. Most of them were priests; one of them was Cheli. After a bit His Excellency came in and we were introduced. We sat down, and I found myself seated between Casaroli and a young Jesuit. I didn't know what to do or say, but this moment of apprehension quickly came to an end when the Jesuit started a conversation having to do with nuclear weapons and nuclear strategy. Casaroli sat pleasantly quiet.

The Jesuit told me that he had come from Harvard, where he had studied international relations at the famed Center for Science and International Affairs, and where Henry Kissinger had resided before going to work for Nixon in 1969. With this illustrious background he had to be well versed in nuclear weapons matters, and he proceeded to give me his views on tactical nuclear weapons and neutron bombs. He held no brief for any of them. He may have been well versed but it became apparent, at least to me, that although his education on nuclear matters was extensive indeed, it hadn't succeeded in bringing him into the real world.

I began to argue with him, more and more intensely. Casaroli remained quiet and, sensing that my spat with the Jesuit was becoming more interesting than their chitchat, the others fell quiet. We went at it, hammer and tongs.

Finally, seeing that we were arguing on the basis of two different strategic perceptions of the world, which made it impossible for either of us to convince each other of the correctness of our views, I decided to ask a direct and specific question of him: "Why don't you like the neutron bomb?"

His answer was equally direct: "It's immoral."

"Why is it immoral?" I asked.

Again, a very direct response: "Because it's a nuclear weapon." And now we had reached the moment of truth.

"Why are nuclear weapons immoral?"

The answer was: "Nuclear weapons are vastly more destructive than high-explosive weapons."*

All of a sudden I had a chance to trip him up on technical grounds, it being impossible to do so in the strategy arena. (Besides, nobody, certainly including me, really understands what nuclear strategy is all about. We've had no nuclear wars so far to lend any empirical base to thinking in this area. Nobody knows how nuclear weapons will work in actual conflict and how soldiers will behave in nuclear conflict. And nobody has even a glimmer of understanding about how nations will behave when caught in the throes of nuclear war.)

First I reminded him of the fact that there are nuclear weapons and nuclear weapons, and that neutron weapons are not like other nuclear weapons. They are nondestructive—they kill but they don't destroy. Therefore, his fundamental premise was wrong. Neutron bombs are not vastly more destructive than high-explosive bombs, they are far less destructive. He must have

* There was nothing new about this attitude in the Church, which going back many hundreds of years, has passed judgment on the morality of new weapons that threatened to disrupt the social order. In this connection I might have reminded the Jesuit that when gunpowder (the first high explosive) appeared in Christendom (coming from China), in the form of the arquebus (a heavy, cumbersome matchlock gun that usually required some form of support to fire the darn thing), the pope took moral offense at this weapon. Now it became possible to kill the policeman of the social order, the knight, with all his protective armor, at a far greater distance than the knight could kill the arquebusier. The pope attempted to excommunicate any arquebusiers who were caught.

known this, of course, graduating from Harvard, but he wasn't about to let a technical fact get in the way of an ideological fixation.

But now my emotions got the best of me, and I let him know that his belief was, in effect, immoral. I sermonized that morality had nothing to do with inanimate things like bombs. People act morally and immorally, which he probably knew very well. I maintained that if he wanted to pass moral judgment on the neutron bomb, he would have to do so in the context of people and nations, war and peace, nations trying to defend themselves against attack by other nations: in other words, in the context of the real world. Still not a peep out of Casaroli.

With my outburst over, the argument was over. The Jesuit was hopping mad at me and didn't care to go on any further. There was a momentary, somewhat strained, silence. Then the others around the table began to talk among themselves. Casaroli rose, thanked me for an enlightening discussion, excused himself and went off to get some sleep. Some days later he sent me a medal from His Holiness, Pope Paul VI.

Getting back to the charge by the young Jesuit that the N-bomb is immoral, since he probably meant to say that its use would be immoral, let's examine its use from a moral standpoint. If we're going to do this, then, as I told the Jesuit, we've got to do it in the real world of human actions and their consequences, not in the confines of theological abstraction. And the real world of human actions pertaining to neutron bombs is: war. Most of us would call war immoral. I sure would, since it always produces suffering, frequently on a monumental scale, and it rarely settles anything. As one war ends, preparations for the next one get under way. I strongly suspect one is getting under way right now, and the thought scares the pants off me. But also to be considered in making moral judgments about war are ideas such as these: Is it moral to defend yourself against unprovoked aggression? Is it moral to determine to fight if one wants to be free? Is it right to cause human suffering during a war, or after the war (where humans include the wounded survivors of the struggle, both ex-soldiers and civilians)? Then, what can be said about the neutron bomb as it relates to these issues?

In our technical discussion of N-bombs, we noted that neutron bombs can spare a city and its inhabitants from destruction and carnage. Hundreds of years of fighting with high-explosive weapons have proved that this can't be accomplished in a conventional war. (Hiroshima and Nagasaki proved that we can accomplish the unspeakable in a war fought with atomic fission weapons such as we now have in our tactical nuclear inventory.) So how can one conclude that using neutrons for battlefield military purposes is immoral as compared with using conventional weapons?

In our technical discussion, we also noted that neutrons don't maim soldiers and civilians. But conventional weapons do. (So will atomic fission weapons, and on a far larger scale than conventional weapons.) Again, why are neutrons immoral as compared with bullets, shrapnel, napalm and other conventional weapons?

The record of conventional defense against aggression in this century has been nothing to brag about, even when it was successful.

In World War I much of Belgium and France was enveloped in battles and suffered terribly: Cities and towns were reduced to rubble, and thousands upon thousands of civilians fled from battle zones. Far worse was the fantastic slaughter of the British and French and German youths, who were fed into the newfangled and murderous machine-gun fire by the hundreds of thousands. True, the Allies finally prevailed and maintained their freedom. But what an awful price they paid. France decided it would never pay such a price again. It set about constructing the Maginot Line to avoid a repetition of the destruction and carnage—especially the carnage. It succeeded by doing a lousy job in constructing the Line. The German tanks rolled through the Ardennes Forest, where the French had decided not to put fortifications, and the war was over in no time at all.

To be sure, the Allies finally managed to beat the Germans again in World War II. But again it was at a fantastic price. Most of Europe went through the horror of Nazi occupation. Then it went through the horror of battles raging over its own territory when the Allies landed on the beaches and fought their way toward Germany. The British, French and American forces suffered more than two million dead and wounded. The Russians suffered more than twenty million dead and wounded. The Germans—who may have been the enemy, but were nevertheless human beings with parents, wives and families—suffered more than ten million dead and wounded. All this was a product of conventional ground warfare.

These two wars had to be immoral to the point of obscenity. And for what? Look what's going on now: We're all getting ready to fight a conventional ground war again. Would it be immoral to use neutrons in a way that would make aggression by enemy ground forces an unpalatable strategy, and thereby deter such aggression?

In April 1951 Representative Albert Gore (D-Tenn.), a member of the JCAE, wrote a long letter to President Harry Truman. The Korean War was going on hot and heavy at that time and the folks back home were becoming less and less tolerant of the idea of American boys spilling their blood for a cause that was becoming more and more confusing. Politicians, especially Democrats, were naturally becoming more and more apprehensive over how the war, if it were still going on the next year, would affect their chances for election and reelection. The President was beginning to realize that his reelection chances were going lower and lower. And so on. (Sure sounds like Vietnam, doesn't it, which some ten years after the Korean War ended, we plunged into with gusto. And taking a look at our present efforts to beef up our conventional forces to "be able to defend ourselves in wars of any size and shape and in any region where we have vital interests," it sure seems that some ten years after the Vietnam War ended, we'll have gotten ourselves into still another one—probably once again in Asia.)

Gore's letter contained a bold new proposal to end the war by means of establishing a radioactive belt across Korea to keep the bad guys from killing the good guys, especially Americans. This was a proposal that he found to be "morally justifiable":

> Korea has become a meat grinder of American manhood. Military authorities, including General Ridgway, have said that under present policies a conclusive military victory is impossible. We must recognize that under present policies our Communist foes have the capacity, what with geo-

> graphic and human preponderances in their favor, to continue this meat-grinder operation indefinitely. We are told that a spring offensive is being mounted now. True, our men have learned better how to meet the foe; true, they will fight bravely; true, enemy losses will be staggering. But what about ours? When is this to end? It is for a solution to this problem that America desperately needs leadership and unity. Something cataclysmic, it seems to me, is called for. We have it. Please consider using it . . .
>
> I suggest therefore:
>
> After removing all Koreans therefrom, dehumanize a belt across the Korean Peninsula by surface radiological contamination. Just before this is accomplished, broadcast the fact to the enemy, with ample and particular notice, that entrance into the belt would mean certain death or slow deformity to all foot soldiers; that all vehicles, weapons, food and apparel entering the belt would be poisoned with radioactivity; and further, that the belt would be regularly recontaminated until such a time as a satisfactory solution to the whole Korean problem shall have been reached. This would differ from the use of the atomic bomb in several ways and would be, I believe, morally justifiable under the circumstances.

Needless to say, President Truman did not respond affirmatively to Congressman Gore's suggestion. However, a couple of years later, Truman's successor, Eisenhower, put an end to the war by threatening to drop atomic bombs on China, which Gore was dead set against.

In 1961, at Senator Dodd's behest, I went to Gore's office (he was now a senator) to brief him on the neutron bomb. By now he had become one of the key arms control figures in the Congress, particularly having to do with the ongoing nuclear test-ban negotiations. Gore and I sat at a table as I flipped through the charts. He listened very attentively, but as I talked, I could see that he was becoming increasingly distressed. When I finished, tears were being shed. The senator was too diplomatic to denounce the Bomb, but he made it clear that its development would symbolize the tragic state of mankind. He had strong moral reservations about such a weapon.

What Senator Gore proposed some thirty years ago was, at that time, not technically doable or militarily practical. Moreover, there were certain features of his proposal that might upset the moral inclinations of many of us: particularly the feature having to do with the "slow deformity" from radioactive poisoning. But even here, the moral point in Gore's favor is that this poisoning wouldn't have been inflicted on the Communist soldiers. They would have inflicted it upon themselves.

The most favorable moral aspect of Senator Gore's proposal was that it was, basically, a peace proposal. He sought to bring hostilities to an end by making it impossible for the combatants to have at each other. The North Koreans and the Chinese would not be able to chase the United Nations forces down the peninsula again, nor would the UN forces be able to chase them back up the peninsula. Is there anything morally wrong with trying to put a barrier between armies so that they can't go on killing each other in a ground war? Or, if there is no war, is there anything morally wrong with trying to put up a barrier that makes it impossible for one side to launch a ground war into the other's territory? In this moral context let's take a look at a technologically updated version of the Gore proposal as it might apply to today's situation in Korea.

Today, assisted by the United States, South Korea has erected a conventional barrier at the 38th Parallel. It is replete with the whole schmear of military fortifications and paraphernalia (minefields, tank traps, barbed wire, etc.) intended to keep the North Korean Army in North Korea. However, given a determined effort by the North, few military experts doubt that, by massing their forces along certain segments of the barrier, the North Koreans could punch through and head south, where the capital of Seoul lies but twenty or thirty miles away. This is not to denigrate the existing barrier, which will serve a valuable purpose in holding up the assault for a while, thereby providing time to move up additional forces to try to stem the tide. But the point to be made is that no conventional barrier is likely to do more than serve as a brief delaying action.

Were war to come again to Korea (and well it might because the tension between the two sides remains high, and North Korea has amassed a formidable army and air force), to one extent or another, the tragedy of the first conflict would be revisited upon the South. Especially tragic would be a revisitation of the battle for Seoul, which left the city so terribly devastated in round one. Seoul, the main artery of the South Korean political-industrial lifeline, has made a tremendous recovery from its ashes of 1951. To have it destroyed again, for want of an adequate defense of South Korea's border, would not only be tragic, it would be senseless. Is there any way South Korea might use neutrons to provide an adequate defense?

Suppose that in front of the South Korean fortifications, and threading through the maze of mines, tank traps, barbed wire and other obstacles, we were to emplace a complex of pipes that would run along the barrier for its entire length. Every so often, say, every half-mile, we would construct an underground chamber, in which we would put a very low-yield neutron warhead. Encasing the chamber would be a hollow shell holding a solution of a chemical compound that contains an element with a large disposition for absorbing neutrons and becoming radioactive (i.e., "induced radioactivity," which we discussed earlier). When the neutron weapon exploded, producing an enormous amount of radioactivity in the solution, the solution would be pumped into the pipes, which would emit gamma rays at a tremendous intensity. With the proper neutron-absorbing element, the period of effective gamma-ray emission could be controlled. For example, a solution containing sodium would provide a militarily effective emission for a few days. A few weeks later the activity would have died down to harmless levels.

Calculations indicate that the intensity would be so great as to make it almost impossible for North Korean soldiers to cross the obstacle zone without picking up a lethal dose of radiation. What makes the gamma rays so effective here is that in trying to make their way through the obstacle zone, a tedious process made more tedious by the firepower directed against them from the fortifications, the invading soldiers are maximizing the time of exposure to the gamma rays. In other words, the obstacles and the firepower coming from the fortifications work to catalyze the effectiveness of the radiation.

To the rear of the barrier we would field a number of short-range missiles, tipped with neutron warheads. These missiles, which could not reach any respectable distance into North Korea, would mainly serve the purpose of dissuading the North Korean forces from massing in an attempt to overwhelm and break through a barrier segment. Were we to shield the fortification personnel from neutrons and gamma rays, which can be accomplished easily and cheaply, since fortifications don't have to move, these neutron warheads could be used with devastating effectiveness against attacking troops (who can't shield themselves). There would be no radiological hazard to the defenders.

Of course, there would be a lot of other military garbage in the overall defensive system: mobile conventional forces to the rear, to cope with attempts to overfly or circumvent the barrier; air defense against enemy bombing and troop-transport aircraft; and what have you. But so much for all this technical-military stuff. Let's suppose that a defensive scheme such as advertised here would really work. How might one weigh this application of neutrons in terms of morality?

On what basis could one morally condemn using neutron weapons if such use succeeded in allowing South Korea to defend itself against aggression, without subjecting its population, towns and cities to the wholesale ravages of ground warfare? On what moral basis could one condemn a gamma-ray version of an electric fence, a purely passive defensive mechanism that seeks to kill nobody, including the aggressor, and leaves the decision to the aggressor whether or not he wants to risk his life by trying to invade through the radiation field?

Let's probe some more into the moral aspects of a barrier, along a defending nation's border, whose effectiveness depends on neutrons.

Historically, one of the most common occasions for war has been a mutual distrust between neighboring countries (like, for example, Israel and its Arab neighbors). In this framework of suspicion, suppose that country A, fearing that its neighbor, country B, is about to attack, decides to preempt and sends its troops marching across the border in a surprise attack. (Take the 1967 war between the Israelis and the Arabs, which resulted in the Israelis gobbling up the Sinai, the Egyptians planning to get it back and staging a surprise attack on Yom Kippur Day of 1973.) Had country B elected to put its military money into a "gamma ray" border defense instead of into a standard armored force holding a highly offensive potential, country A never would have had cause to fear attack from B in the first place. Barriers can't march. The war could have been avoided, since B's military posture would invalidate the dark distrust of A. Putting the shoe on the other foot, if A really feared B all that much, why wouldn't A want to put up its own gamma-ray fence? In fact, were both sides to do this, in essence, a *de facto* nonaggression pact would be in effect, even though one or both sides still might harbor distrust and dislike for the other. Moreover, were both sides to do this, it could be done a helluva lot more cheaply than producing big armies to go marching across borders. That is, unless both sides, down deep inside their national psyches, preferred to fight. Unfortunately I suspect this is more likely to be the case than not.

As for any walk of life, there are Catholic bishops and Catholic bishops. There were the Catholic bishops of the United States who, in 1968, issued a corporate opinion morally condemning the neutron bomb:

> . . . Nothing more dramatically suggests the antilife direction of technological warfare than the neutron bomb; one philosopher declares that the manner in which it would leave entire cities intact, but totally without life, makes it perhaps the symbol of our civilization. It would be perverse indeed if the Christian conscience were to be unconcerned or mute in the face of the multiple moral aspects of these awesome prospects.

Certainly, with no intent of impugning in any way the good faith of the bishops, and please forgive me, one notices the remarkable similarity between this and moral denunciations made by Soviet spokesmen. Where there is a difference, it lies in the obvious misperception by the bishops on what the neutron bomb is supposed to do and a deliberate distortion of this function by Soviet propagandists.

However, in 1981 the Catholic bishops of Connecticut deliberated on the moral aspects of nuclear weapons, nuclear war, the nuclear arms race, and reached some fascinating conclusions pertinent to the nuclear barrier scheme just discussed, although they hardly had this scheme in mind when they did so. In this connection the bishops posed two key questions for deliberation: "(1) Is it moral for a nation to possess nuclear arms?; (2) Is it moral for a nation to manufacture and sell nuclear arms to other nations?" Here are the results of their deliberations:

> Is it moral for a nation to possess nuclear arms? The Second Vatican Council, after lamenting the inhumanity of war, states: "As long as the danger of war remains and there is no competent and sufficiently powerful authority, at the international level, governments cannot be denied the right to legitimate defense once every means of peaceful settlement has been exhausted. State authorities and others who share public responsibility have the duty to conduct such grave matters soberly and to protect the people entrusted to their care.
>
> From this we conclude that it is moral for any nation to possess nuclear arms if these are possessed for self-defense only. We cannot expect a nation to be a conscientious objector, to refuse to defend itself. We wish that all nations would abjure armaments. But if one does not, the others have the right to arm themselves. And if others possess or will possess nuclear arms, a nation has the right to possess nuclear arms for self-defense.
>
> Let there be an absolute condemnation of any "first-strike" strategy.
>
> Is it moral for a nation to manufacture and to sell nuclear arms to others? This question was not even considered by the Second Vatican Council. However, the answer seemingly would follow from the previous teaching. If a nation has a right to possess arms for defense, that nation has the right to produce arms for its own defense. If a nation has a right to possess arms for defense, it has a right to buy arms for defense produced in another country. If other countries have the right to possess or produce arms for their own defense, a nation has the right to sell to other countries arms for their defense.

Clearly the above pronouncements do not attach a moral opprobrium to the use of neutron weapons for self-defense (which would obviously include barrier application). However, they seem to go one step beyond this; they provide moral sanction to the possibility of a country actually *selling* neutron weapons to another country, provided the weapons are to be used strictly for self-defense. In other words, were the United States to sell neutron warheads to South Korea, or Israel, or even West Germany, on the assurance that they would be used only for self-defense, the Connecticut bishops would offer no moral objections.

One way to provide assurance that the warheads would not be misused would be for the United States to demand in advance that countries desiring these warheads commit themselves to building nuclear barriers at their borders and actually build them. Upon completion, we would then sell them the warheads. Since such construction would represent quite an expensive undertaking, this would seem to be an assurance given in pretty good faith.

If such a commitment still didn't satisfy us, we could design the neutron warheads to make it very difficult for the recipient country to use them for offensive purposes. This could be accomplished by making the warheads pretty darned heavy. For the warheads to be emplaced underground for the purpose of generating radioactivity, the weight would be of no consequence, since the warheads wouldn't have to be delivered anywhere. However, for incorporation into the missiles deployed in the rear, the added weight would constitute a considerable penalty as far as its design and performance were concerned, and would substantially hike its cost. On the other hand, if this is the price of deterring war, well—so be it.

Now we've got to realize that the fantasy of Uncle Sam selling neutron bombs to other countries is exactly that—a fantasy. This is because there's a law against it, and the United States holds itself to being a law-abiding nation. The law is the nuclear Non-Proliferation Treaty (NPT), ratified by the United States in 1970, and it is based on the strong belief, as stated in the treaty, that "the proliferation of nuclear weapons would seriously enhance the danger of nuclear war." Since most Americans believe that nuclear war represents a moral abomination, in the framework of the NPT, selling neutron bombs would be morally wrong. It would be morally wrong even if such sales would seriously enhance prospects for peace around the world. Or is the NPT morally wrong in part? Confusing, isn't it?

Making the moral issue of this nuclear arms sale even more confusing is the fact that the United States has had no official compunction in selling billions and billions of dollars worth of conventional weapons to countries that have used them to bomb the cities of other countries and kill and maim their soldiers. To be sure, many well-meaning and even morally motivated Americans have striven to have their country cut down on its "Merchants of Death" activity. But they have had precious little effect on arms sales, which have recently been increasing apace. And we know very well that in selling these munitions to various countries, many of the buyers will use them against other countries sooner or later. But even to consider selling them nuclear weapons is, come to think of it, *unthinkable.* It's immoral. I don't get it.

"Any act of war aimed at the indiscriminate destruction of entire cities along with their populations is a crime against God and man himself. It merits unequivocal, and unhesitating, condemnation." Thus stated the Connecticut bishops. I fully concur. My government never has. Even such a God-fearing man as President Jimmy Carter threatened the Russians with such destruction in the event that they attacked us, declaring, in his 1979 State of the Union address: "Just one of our relatively invulnerable Poseidon submarines—comprising less than two percent of our total nuclear force of submarines, aircraft and land-based missiles—carries enough warheads to destroy every large- and medium-sized city in the Soviet Union." This is a terrible threat for any government official to make, let alone a U.S. President. It is a terrible thing for any country to have to base its military strategy on the massacre of an enemy's civilian population. It is grossly immoral. It goes against the grain of all civilized human values. Even Henry Kissinger, the great amoralist on international power politics, has recoiled against such a policy: "We live in the paradoxical world that it is precisely the liberal, humane, progressive community that is advocating the most bloodthirsty strategies and insisting that there is nothing to worry about as long as the capacity exists to kill one hundred million people."

It would appear that these horrendous observations on our strategic nuclear policy have little, if anything, to do with neutron bombs. That's true; they don't. I was only trying to make a point about nuclear morality having to do with one country nuclear bombing the cities of another country. What I was leading up to, however, was the notion of using neutron warheads strategically, as an alternative to the civil carnage and "city busting" that result from using A-bombs and H-bombs. In this context I want to revisit the case of country A worrying about being attacked by country B, but where country A wanted to deter attacks on its cities by threatening a nuclear response of a different kind, leading to results other than the demolition of cities and the extermination of civilians.

What I have in mind here is an alternative weapons concept that would do nothing in the way of death and destruction to the civilian fabric of an enemy country. Along these lines we shall now introduce another N-bomb. This time N is for Nothing, but not necessarily good for nothing.

Here's the nothing bomb. Since we examined the nuclear barrier application in the framework of South Korea trying to dissuade North Korea from attacking, let's apply the nothing bomb to the same situation.

Suppose that far to the rear of the demilitarized zone, way down the peninsula, as far away as possible from North Korean air bases, South Korea built a handful of special facilities. Each facility would have the following makeup and functions:

First, an underground chamber, in which to explode a very low-yield neutron warhead. The arrangement would be similar to that envisaged for producing radioactivity for the nuclear barrier. The only significant difference would be that instead of producing a radioactive solution to be pumped into pipes, the goal here is to produce millions of very small (BB-sized) radioactive pellets, to be poured into the nose cones of missiles.

Once produced, the irradiated and now extremely radioactive pellets would be removed from the chamber and stored, again underground, near the missile. The missile also would be underground, in a hardened silo like our ICBMs. (In fact, by having everything underground, not only would the facility be heavily protected against enemy attack, but the radiation shielding attained by a lot of earth and concrete would make it safe for operating personnel at the surface. The shielding analogy here would be that of a nuclear power reactor which is heavily shielded to allow operating personnel to do their chores safely.) Here they would stay until the war started, if it ever did.

Assume the war is on. At this point the pellets would be poured into the missile nose cone, which would have a special dispensing mechanism in order to release them uniformly over the target area—say, a North Korean city. The button is pushed and off go the missiles. As the nose cones reenter the atmosphere over the city, the dispensing mechanism ejects the pellets, which come wafting down to the surface at velocities not too much higher than the current U.S. national speed limit (55 mph).

Those in the city now have a dilemma on their hands. If they want to stay put, after a few days they will be risking radiation damage (from the gamma rays) to themselves. On the other hand, if they decide to get out of town, they are going to have to face up to the hardships of living out of town, but they certainly won't be endangering their lives to nearly the same degree. (Of course, the evacuation of cities would be nothing new to the North Koreans.)

Which option—stay or leave—might be picked up by the North Koreans? Take your choice. I'd get out of there as soon as I could pack some belongings, and take my chances someplace else. One way or another, however, sooner or later the functions of the city would come to a halt. They would come to a permanent halt were the residents to stay on until they killed themselves. But this would be at their own perverse insistence. They would come to a temporary halt, say, for a few weeks (at which time the radiation would have died down to safe levels), if the residents pulled out shortly after the pellets came down on the city. They would only stay out if, in the meantime, the North Koreans decided to stop fighting. If they didn't, another radioactive payload could be dispatched to deny the city for a few more weeks. You can go on with your scenarizing if you wish, but I'm stopping mine right here.

Since we're supposed to be discussing neutronic morality, where does this concept fit in, in the moral scheme of things? Darned if I know, but I do have a few observations to make.

First of all, I'd say that this punitive measure makes a lot more sense than blasting a city to smithereens and massacring its people by nuclear bombing. However, I'd also say that it makes more sense than conducting conventional bombing attacks on the city that, if done enough times, or on a large enough scale, can have the same net result as a nuclear weapons attack. (I suspect that anyone who survived the attacks on Hamburg, or Dresden, or

Tokyo, or Yokahama, during World War II would not disagree with this.)

Secondly, although the Connecticut bishops might not look too kindly on this scheme because it is offensive and directed toward civilians, nevertheless the scheme does not in any way conform to an "act of war aimed indiscriminately at the destruction of entire cities of extensive areas along with their population," which the bishops hold to be morally criminal. In fact, we seem to have the opposite situation here. This scheme is highly discriminate and involves no destruction of cities and their populations.

Finally, in morally judging the scheme, we have to think of long-term consequences, as well as what is happening during the war. Granted that an urban population forced to evacuate their city for a few weeks, or even longer, is going to go through a miserable period. But when the war is over and they return, they will be coming back to just about what they left. The city will be intact.

In June 1979 Dick Cella called me in Washington, D.C., where I was on business. The pope had appointed a number of cardinals. One of them was Casaroli. Not only was Casaroli about to become a cardinal, he was also about to become Vatican secretary of state. An American contingent (not including the Harvard Jesuit) headed by Cheli (who had been promoted to archbishop since I last saw him), was going to Rome to join in the elevation ceremonies. I was invited. Would I come immediately? I left that afternoon for New York. That night we flew to Rome. What happened next had to be the most meaningful and moving experience of my professional existence. For a person who has spent most of his career creating and promoting new nuclear weapons concepts, it was an amazing experience.

No sooner had we gotten off the airplane, checked into our hotel and freshened up, than Cella and I headed for the Vatican to join Archbishop Cheli and a nice monsignor from Brooklyn, and off we went to meet Casaroli at his Vatican apartment. Casaroli wanted to welcome us to the Holy City and spent an hour of pleasant chatter with us. (Having been caught unawares by Cella, I had but two suits to my name—one of them a seersucker, which was the least dirty and which I wore to Casaroli's apartment. Cella, who had had plenty of time to select an appropriate wardrobe for the occasion, naturally wore a black—clerical black—suit. Rarely have I felt so out of place.)

The next morning we went off to a huge auditorium on the Vatican grounds to attend the investiture ceremonies for the new cardinals. Onstage were all the cardinals from all over the world. My eyes were popping out of my head. I'd never seen a cardinal before. After a while a tremendous cheer went up; the pope was coming onstage. The ceremonies began, the cardinals-elect appeared one by one (Casaroli, about to become Number 2 in the hierarchy, was called up first) to receive their scrolls and join the other cardinals. It was quite an affair.

The ceremonies at an end, Cella, the Brooklyn monsignor and I got into a car, and with Cheli driving we went off to a Catholic orphanage for a lunch in Casaroli's honor. Preceding the lunch was a reception, where a number of cardinals (close to Casaroli, I would imagine) mingled with the guests. Naturally almost everyone was Italian. Whereas I certainly didn't feel unwelcome in such a gathering, I did feel out of place. I angled toward the bar, in need of a stiff drink, but had to settle for a Campari. Cella noticed my discomfiture and pulled me off into a corner where I could gab and relax with him, but not for long.

Up came Cheli, took my arm and told me that he wanted me to meet some of the prelates. The first one was a little Italian cardinal who looked like he'd be blown away by a stiff wind, which he probably wished had happened before he met me. "Your Eminence," said Cheli, in English, "may I introduce Sam Cohen. He is the Father of the Neutron Bomb." The poor guy practically went into a state of shock. So did I. Not in a million years—down here or up there—did the cardinal ever expect such an introduction. Not in a million years—down here, certainly not up there—did I ever expect to be so-introduced to a man of the cloth who didn't know me from Adam.

I didn't know what the hell to say. Cheli stood there, smiling beatifically. But the cardinal recovered enough to put on a sickly smile and say: "You must be a terrible person." Now I was really speechless. What could I say? Cheli now stepped in and answered for me: "No, Your Eminence, I can assure you that Mr. Cohen is a highly moral person." This floored me as least as much as the introduction. Somehow I managed to recover, as did His Eminence, and entered into a brief conversation. By now I *really* needed a stiff drink, which I wasn't about to get. Instead, Cheli steered me away and up to another cardinal and went through the same introduction. And still again, a few more times. To put it mildly, I was dumbfounded.

A couple of days later I arose very early and again went to the Vatican, which I was getting to know pretty well by now. The pope was going to conduct a special mass in honor of Cardinal Casaroli. I had been invited, along with a few dozen of Casaroli's guests, relatives and Vatican clerical colleagues. We gathered at a small garden chapel outside a house where His Holiness was residing temporarily. An inveterate infidel, and now really feeling out of place, I made a beeline for the back row of seats. (If lightning was going to strike me during mass, I wanted the pope to be as far away from me as possible; he was freshly aboard and his immediate predecessor was barely aboard when he died.) But this was not to be. Archbishop Cheli saw me back there, came up to me, escorted me to the front row and sat me down.

A few minutes later the pope came out and conducted mass just a few feet from where I sat. The mass over, His Holiness mingled with the audience. I stood there not knowing what to do with myself. Dick Cella had left earlier to go home, and my psychological crutch went with him. However, I didn't stand there very long. Casaroli came up to me and asked me if I had met His Holiness. Before I could say I hadn't, which I suspect he knew, he took me by the arm and squired me over to Pope John Paul II. And if you're wondering whether he repeated the same, by now standard, introduction, the answer is "Yeah!"

Unlike the little cardinal who a couple of days earlier had trembled in the presence of the devil incarnate, His Holiness couldn't have played it cooler. If he was at all startled, there was no sign. We shook hands, I expressed my great pleasure in meeting him, and then he asked me: "I trust you are working for peace?" What could I say? I told him I was, as best I could, in my own way, and added that I was certainly inspired by his efforts in this direction. We chatted for a few minutes and then he had to greet still another guest. A few minutes after that I said good-bye to my hosts, went back to the hotel, checked out and headed home.

CHAPTER 8
JUMPING SHIP

LAST SPRING I WAS INVITED to join a local TV talk show for a discussion of the nuclear freeze movement, which was gaining tremendous momentum in Los Angeles. (Even the local politicians were beginning to realize that concern over global nuclear war and being profreeze were good local politics, and the LA city council had just voted 12–1 in favor of freezing.) There were several guests on the show and they appeared individually to face questioning by the hosts. I was third and had to cool my heels in the waiting room while the first two went on. There was a television set in the waiting room so I could watch the show as I waited.

The first guest appeared: she was a Japanese woman who had been in Hiroshima at the time the Bomb went off. She was now fifty years old; twelve at the time of the bombing, but looked far younger than her years. At the time of the bombing she had decided to hate all Americans. But later on she met one of the crew of the bomber that had done in her home town and he told her that he was terribly sorry and remorseful for what he had done. So she stopped hating Americans. However, I wondered whether, if she were to meet me and find out that I had worked on the Bomb during the war, she would shoot me a look of hatred. And I began to get very queasy; I don't like to be hated.

Finally it was my turn to go on and, sure enough, the very first question I got was: "Do you ever feel guilty about having worked on the Bomb that did those terrible things to Hiroshima?" My answer was: "No!" Then I explained why.

Six years before the bombing, her country had attacked Pearl Harbor, forcing us into a war with Japan that we might have avoided otherwise. My country had to mobilize a huge army and send it all the way across the Pacific to defeat her country. That's what war was all about in those days: defeating the enemy. At the time we dropped the atomic bomb on Hiroshima, we were moving millions of American soldiers into position to assault the Japanese islands. If the Bomb had not brought the Japanese to their knees, we were prepared to accomplish this through invasion. And the military estimates were that this could readily result in upwards of a million American casualties. As an American, caring far more about my countrymen than her countrymen, why in heaven's name would I want to feel guilty about something that had saved all those American lives?

I don't suggest that the President and the Congress were doing something terribly wrong in planning for the invasion of Japan. Obviously they thought they were doing the right thing and there was certainly no indication from the American people that they thought otherwise. There was no demand that we promptly bring the boys home. Instead, the people continued to express full support for whatever the government chose to do (although I wonder how supportive the GIs, especially those who had already survived combat in Europe and in the Pacific, might have been). But there was this unanswered question as to whether invading the Japanese islands was really the best thing to do for the country. Or was it maybe that the country still hadn't gotten enough war out of its system? I don't know, but I've often wondered.

I especially wonder these days when I see the United States building up its conventional forces lickety-split to be able to dispatch them thousands of miles away at a moment's notice to do battle with the Red Army for the most implausible reasons. Unless there are deeper reasons, such as liking a good war now and then to get the country's juices flowing. Maybe there are some underlying motivations that have caused wars throughout man's history, despite the fact that for thousands of years civilized man has possessed a rational mind that, one would think, could recognize war's basic irrationality and at least take steps to try to avoid it—but hasn't. The wars keep coming.

Any way you care to slice it, war has to be an irrational, uncivilized act. In fact, the more civilized a nation claims to be, the more irrational it is to go to war. On what rational grounds, unless it is attacked directly and has to fight for its survival, can an ostensibly civilized country, holding to genteel religious beliefs, go to war?

To protect "vital interests," i.e., economic interests? Take a look at the wars the United States has gotten into in this century. How has the national bank account balanced out as a result of these wars? You know the answer: very negatively. Wars are fantastically expensive affairs. This "vital interests" baloney is exactly that—baloney. That is, unless we act like the imperialists the Russians claim we are, which we're not about to do. If we save the Saudis' oil by going to war, the way we behave, we'd only do this so they could go on gouging us with higher oil prices.

To protect freedom? Well, that used to sound like a good idea until we tried to protect the freedom of the South Vietnamese and found out that our efforts were costing too much blood and, perish the thought, too much money. The price of somebody else's freedom turned out to be too high. The Vietnam War was in no small way responsible for our current economic woes. In World

War I we helped to free much of continental Europe from the Germans and made a big point of this in rationalizing our involvement and in establishing our national pride. Then, some two decades later, continental Europe was enslaved by one of the worst tyrannies in history. Those whose freedom we helped obtain in World War I seemed to have practically an instinctual drive to lose it again. In World War II we again freed Europe, which again is working toward losing its freedom. We freed the Chinese from the barbaric Japanese only to have them become slaves to Chinese Communists, whose barbarism, in maintaining the new order, was at least as bad as that of the Japanese. Then the Japanese became our ally, for whom we seem willing to commit suicide in order to keep *them* free from the Communists. And so on.

We could go on here about why we go to war, and how ridiculous it usually is when we go to war. But we won't. The point I'm trying to make here is that unless we're attacked, going to war makes little sense, and in the long run (frequently, the short run), it solves nothing in the grand scheme of things.

War is an irrational business, which the politicians who get us into them never stop to contemplate. Even were the scholars to come up with a foolproof explanation of the root case, the people and their political leaders would refuse to believe it. My own belief, which I'll expound upon here, is that the most rational way to avoid getting into an irrational act is: Don't get into it. The best way for us to avoid war is: Avoid war. But we're not doing this. To the contrary, we're heading right down the primrose path into another war, which I fear terribly will be a nuclear war. If that happens in our current state of defenselessness against nuclear attack, well—that's all, folks.

If nuclear weapons had never existed, I might be tempted to say: "What the hell, if we want to be irrational enough to go to war, or better yet, irrational enough to *want* to go to war, let's go to war. Let's send our young men overseas and cheer them on as they get shot up. We'll survive, and if this is the way the country wants to get its kicks, let it." But I can't say that, because there are thousands of Soviet nuclear weapons that can kill us back here and wipe out the whole country—my country, your country, our country. We've got to stay out of war.

* * *

If I sound like a crazy alarmist, all that I can say is that I have good company: my fellow countrymen. Major pollsters have been asking their respondents what they think about the U.S.A. getting into another war and how the war might be fought. The results have been absolutely mind-boggling. They represent a drastic switch from attitudes expressed only several years ago when, with Vietnam still fresh in mind, they were dead set against foreign involvement and felt that the political leaders would get the message and keep us out of war.

By large majorities, two- and three-to-one, Americans are now more concerned about a major war with the Russians than a limited war with somebody else. This, of course, should be the proper way to feel, since the Russians can kill us off as a sovereign state. Most of us feel that if we do start a fight with the Russians, it cannot be limited to conventional weapons; it will go nuclear. And if it does, the majority of us think it will be all-out nuclear war, which can be roughly translated into *our national demise.* The administration could not be more out of tune with the people in persisting with its efforts to build up its conventional forces to fight conventional wars with the Russians.

Although most of the American people do not choose to pin a nuclear warmongering label on the current administration, more than half feel there is a chance of all-out nuclear war with the Russians within the next ten years. This really has to be incredible. Until very recently our political leaders have labeled nuclear war as "inconceivable." Now, all of a sudden, the majority of population finds it VERY conceivable indeed.

One can draw any number of conclusions one desires from these results about the possibility of nuclear war. Since polls unto themselves hardly constitute crystal balls, it would seem illogical for one to take their conclusions too seriously. Moreover, we want to keep in mind that all the great Delphians who have been predicting nuclear war over the last few decades have turned out to be prophets of dubious honor.

On the other hand, I would attach great importance to these polling results, which reflect the feeling of a rather honorable American society.

These polls may reflect a lot more than simple uneducated

guesses, which, I can assure you, having been in this nuclear warfare business from the beginning, are every bit as good as the educated guesses of profound strategic thinkers. They may also reflect how people are feeling, but not "thinking," way down deep about war and what they want way down deep: like war, maybe. The wish is father to the thought. I've got a sneaking hunch that in our national unconscious, we've got a strong national urge to go to war again. The trouble is that, in the Nuclear Age, this is tantamount to a strong national death wish.

If the majority of the people think there's a fair chance of nuclear war with the Soviet Union within the next ten years, then why aren't they demanding that their political leaders make sure we don't get into one? Instead, once again, we're blindly taking the word of our leaders that everything possible is being done to avoid war with the Soviet Union. We have never stopped to think that proclaiming something won't happen doesn't necessarily keep it from happening. We have never stopped to think that maybe our great leaders don't really know what they're doing and that maybe they're doing more to get us into a war than to keep us out of one. Think of all the political leaders of the past who pledged to keep us out of war but did just the opposite. And we don't seem to have the wildest idea what is being implied when our Secretary of Defense, to explain the reason for our massive conventional force buildup, states:

> We must frankly recognize the possibility of a similar military operation [a Soviet invasion of Europe] against other countries where the Western interest would be vital. In the middle of any night I may be awakened to be told that the Soviet Union is actually in the process of invading a country that we must defend, but where we have neither bases nor troops. . . . This is why I put so much stress on improving our ability to mobilize our forces and to mobilize quickly. We may not again have the preparation time we had to get ready for World War II, which was barely enough then.
>
> Conventional wars could come in all sizes; if we value our freedom, we must be able to defend ourselves in wars of any size and shape and in any region where we have

> vital interests. That means developing urgently a better ability to respond to crises far from our shores, and to stay there as long as necessary. The West's dependence on [Persian Gulf] oil means that we must make sure we can respond effectively to threats in this region.*

With respect to the Secretary's remarks, and what the Defense Department has in mind about using our conventional forces against the Russians, please allow me to tell another story.

In June 1981, along with about two hundred civilians from all walks of life, I went off to the U.S. Army War College to attend their annual national security seminar. The purpose of the seminar was to bring ordinary people together with extraordinary military officers (who are in line to become generals) attending the War College, to discuss matters of war and peace. The way the shindig went was to have a distinguished guest give a speech to all of us in the morning, which would be discussed that afternoon by the seminar participants.

One of the guest speakers was a ranking official from the Pentagon, who explained the administration's new policies for defending our "vital interests" around the world. This meant, among other things, explaining the purpose of the Rapid Deployment Force, which the Carter administration had originated, and which the Reagan administration wanted to expand greatly. Naturally the most vital interest to be defended was the oil from the Persian Gulf.

The official informed us that the Pentagon had calculated the cost of fighting the Soviet Union for control of the Gulf (strictly in terms of a conventional war). The estimate was that in such a war our defense budget would have to be increased to about one trillion dollars a year. He personally thought the price tag would be much higher. But whatever the cost might be, it was so vital to preserve the flow of Gulf oil that the United States really had no choice but to foot the bill. He continued talking about defending the Gulf.

At one point he mentioned how much oil the Saudis were pumping: about ten million barrels a day. Since the Saudis pump

* From a speech delivered to the United Press International Luncheon of the American Newspaper Publishers Association meeting, Chicago, Illinois, May 5, 1981.

the bulk of the Gulf oil and we're primarily interested in defending Saudi Arabia, suddenly I had a yardstick for comparison. I now shut the speaker out of my mind and began to calculate.

Let's see, they're pumping 10 million barrels a day, and if we suppose they pump almost every day of the year, then we have about 3.5 billion barrels a year. If we further suppose that just before the war starts, they're gouging us at the rate of, say, thirty bucks a barrel, then the oil pumped per year costs out at something like a hundred billion dollars. Now, that's an awful lot of money by itself, but not so much when we compare it with how much money the speaker thought Uncle Sam would have to shell out each year to fight the Russians, to preserve the oil for our side. And to preserve Saudi profits and whatever profits the oil companies might make.

If the speaker's estimate was at all correct, we're willing to pump nearly ten times as much money into a war, to save the oil, as the oil is worth. Now that just doesn't make very much sense. It has to be plain nonsense. And if we add to our military cost the cost in blood of our soldiers and the cost in domestic upheaval, the whole business seems downright irrational. Moreover, if we take into account that the official gave us no guarantee that this would win the war—in fact, winning never even entered the discussion, although President Reagan, when campaigning, had said that if he committed the nation to war, he would commit us to victory—it begins to appear almost insane.

As a matter of fact, if we take into account that the Russians, completely apart from trying to take over the Gulf oil facilities, can deny the flow of oil by bombing either the facilities or the tankers from the USSR, we can scratch the "almost." It *is* insane. There's not a thing we can do to stop such bombing by the Russians unless we want to attack their bases in the USSR. This means nuclear war with them. And that would be the end of us.

If fighting in Southwest Asia is the major purpose for building up our conventional forces, via the Rapid Deployment Forces, and the application of these forces has been so poorly thought out, why is the Pentagon up to this lunacy? Unless it wants to fight. Why has the Congress overwhelmingly approved a military budget that substantially expands our conventional forces (which the Defense Department has called "the most usable of military power")? And why have the American people, after suffering through the debacle of Vietnam, seemingly placed such blind trust in their government as it builds up its conventional forces in order to fight another war? Especially when the majority of us think the next war will be an all-out nuclear war? It doesn't make sense unless the country wants another war.

Instead of blindly, or maybe instinctively, supporting an extremely expensive, massive conventional arms buildup, why don't the American people demand, for the sake of our survival, that we stay out of the Persian Gulf, or any other place where we might come up against Soviet military might? Not only can we not hack it economically, (*however else*) we might very well get ourselves killed if we try. We can get along without Gulf oil. Sure, it might call for some belt tightening; but it's a lot better to carpool than to go to war stupidly. Better yet, to avoid such inconveniences, why don't we start stockpiling oil like mad? It will be vastly cheaper than paying for a war to preserve it.

Maybe our NATO allies can't get along without the oil. But you don't see them offering to dispatch military forces to help us help them preserve Gulf oil. They're selfish enough, or sensible enough, or both, to want to stay out of such a war. How crazy can we be?

Before becoming the first chairman of the Atomic Energy Commission, David Lilienthal had been a prime mover in the U.S. government in the area of nuclear arms control and disarmament. He had been chairman of the advisory panel to the State Department on international control of nuclear weapons, and was instrumental to helping to draw up the famous Baruch Plan, one of whose objectives was to rid the world of nuclear weapons.

Seventeen years later Lilienthal was disillusioned by his initial idealism. In March of 1963 he journeyed to Princeton University to deliver a speech entitled "The Mythology of Nuclear Disarmament." In his speech he made the following observation:

> The basic atomic weapons policy of the United States from almost the beginning days of Hiroshima has been based upon a fundamental but quite understandable misapprehension.

> What is the essence of this great misapprehension? It is this: That because the Atom is such a uniquely powerful force for destruction, a revolutionary kind of destructive power, in dealing with it we must divorce it, set it apart, from everything the human race has previously learned about man's behavior, about war and peace, about our institutions, about foreign policy, about military matters, about science. This simply isn't so . . . we have already learned, the hard way, that it isn't so. But being misled by this belief in the special status of the powerful Atom, we have increasingly brought upon ourselves frustration after frustration.
>
> The fantastic destructive power of the Atom is a reality. The conclusions drawn from this fact are myths.
>
> Those myths are still at the foundation of our policies and our outlook.

The myths Lilienthal spoke of twenty years ago are still with us, and they control our nuclear policies today. In perpetuating them, we have practically guaranteed the undoing of our major allies, NATO in particular. And we have placed the survival of our country in increasing peril. The reason why was explained recently by Harold Brown when he was Secretary of Defense: "Nothing in the [U.S.] policy contemplates that nuclear war can be a deliberate instrument for achieving our national security goals, because it cannot be." In other words, it is pointless to use nuclear weapons to fight a war. For the last twenty years this has been the essence of our nuclear policy. It has not only guided our defense, but that of our allies as well.

For reasons never explained, the United States has adopted policies for nuclear weapons that assume that with the dawn of the Nuclear Age, human beings underwent a miraculous transformation, that a class of weapons had come upon earth that so terrified humanity, that people and nations would divest themselves of the bellicose behavior they had shown throughout human history. People simply would not fight with these weapons. As Lilienthal said, we have "set [nuclear weapons] apart from everything the human race has previously learned about man's behavior." By mythological fiat, U.S. policy makers claim to have effected a fundamental change in the human psyche.

This miraculous change may be true on our side—although it

really isn't, because given a really traumatic situation, like a war we're losing, where our military forces are being skunked, we'll use them all right. However, it takes two to tàngo. And for our policy to hold water, the other side has to go along. It probably won't; it never has. The Soviets never have regarded the advent of nuclear weapons as having a fundamental impact on human nature. Instead, they have regarded them as having had a "revolutionary" impact on war, which is in direct contrast to our way of looking at it. To quote from Soviet military doctrine: "The [nuclear] revolution in military affairs is an accomplished fact. It led to basic quantitative and qualitative changes in the military-technological base of the armed forces and its structure. It marked a revolution in the methods of waging war, a revolution in the theory of military art and actual combat training of troops." In other words, the Russian idea is to train and exercise their military forces in the use of nuclear weapons.

Basic U.S. policy may claim that there "cannot be" a relationship between our political objectives and the employment of nuclear weapons. Contrast this to basic Soviet policy claims (again quoting from their doctrine) which state: ". . . the relationship between politics and war, thoroughly revealed in the writings of Lenin, not only remains valid in the Nuclear Age, but acquires even greater significance." This fundamental assymetry in policy and doctrine—a mythology on our side versus a realistic acceptance of men and nations for what they are and what they have been on the other side—says all there is to be said about how bleak our future is. Unless we change our ways of thinking about the Bomb. Given this fundamental assymetry on how the two sides think about nuclear weapons, given the fact that we don't know how to use nuclear weapons in war (because we don't want to know how) while the Soviets do, and given that nuclear war is a distinct possibility—as Americans now view it, and as the Russians have always viewed it—may God protect us from the Godless Soviets, because we seem hell-bent on not protecting ourselves.

If our current plans to fight in the Persian Gulf seem to be lacking in rationality, the same has held true for our plans to defend Europe for the last twenty years. Underlying our irrationality about defending NATO has been our steadfast refusal to incorporate nuclear weapons into our basic doctrine, while the Soviets have been basing their doctrine on such incorporation. To show you how irrational the NATO military thinking is, let me explain the strategy that forms the basis of NATO's defense. The strategy is predicated on the following war scenario:

PHASE I:

The Soviets finally decide to attack Europe, but by using conventional weapons only. Having so decided, they begin a massive mobilization of the Warsaw Pact forces. This is a time-consuming business, taking as much as a week, or two, or three to get all their forces ready. At the same time this gives NATO a good chance to prepare its defenses: The troops can be moved out of the casernes and dispatched toward the Iron Curtain to meet the expected assault, the aircraft can be scattered over a much larger number of air bases to increase their survivability against attack by enemy aircraft and missiles, the nuclear warheads and their delivery systems can be removed from their peacetime storage locations and dispersed into the field, the United States can begin to fly men and equipment across the Atlantic to buttress its forces already in Europe. And so it goes.

PHASE II:

The war begins, with a massive armored assault, blitzkrieg style—the Soviet game plan—across the North German plain. Since the Warsaw Pact has long had superior conventional war capabilities, the expectation is that they will go like gangbusters, and before you know it, they will be almost a third of the way into West Germany. (Of course, to prevent this from happening, NATO has forever been beseeching itself to strengthen its conventional forces. But the normal peacetime urge of putting butter ahead of guns has prevailed, and today NATO remains as far behind the Pact as ever, with absolutely no signs that this situation will change.) The Russians have to be stopped. It is now or never. And this is where battlefield nuclear weapons—including neutron bombs, assuming we had been able to dispatch any over there—

now come into play. Using a number of these weapons against the onrushing Soviet tank armies, it is hoped that the attack will be blunted, and the Soviets, now badly hurt and realizing that their foolishness has gotten them into a *nuclear* war, will see the sweet light of reason, break off the war and come to the conference table to salvage what they can. Otherwise, NATO may counterattack, now using the dreaded neutron weapons to drive them out of Western Europe—even though the United States government has said these weapons have no offensive capability. Hallelujah! The war is over. And mind you, talk about good nuclear manners, the Soviets have not used even one nuclear weapon.*

But suppose something goes awry and the Russians keep coming, despite the nuclear battering their tank armies have taken.

PHASE III:

The United States, living up to its pledges to NATO Europe, now begins to conduct thermonuclear attacks on the Soviet homeland to convince them of the folly of their ways, so that they'll stop invading Europe. If this ploy works, well—Hallelujah! The war is over. But suppose that it doesn't. What then?

Well, it might happen that the Soviets become provoked for the first time. The ever-patient Russian Bear is finally mad enough to use nuclear weapons against us, in the United States, because we nuked him; and against NATO forces in Europe, because they nuked his forces. At this juncture the future of the United States and Europe is not too bright. Our country is totally vulnerable to nuclear attack, and NATO, never having learned to fight with nuclear weapons, will be creamed in short order by the Soviet forces, who have learned how to use them.

Now, if your mouth is hanging wide open in stark disbelief over what I've just described, I don't blame you. Maybe you don't want to believe me. However, all I can say is that what I've described above is essentially official NATO strategy, the so-called

* This is a scenario similar to one published recently by a best-selling British general.

flexible-response strategy. What I've related *all* comes from official U.S. and NATO government documents, available to anyone interested. My interest has been a long-standing professional one, which is why I've kept up with it all.

Does this scenario really reflect the Soviet strategy for going to war with NATO? Of course not! If one takes the time to go through the Soviet military doctrinal literature, he will see that, point by point, the NATO strategy is rendered invalid.

Former Soviet Defense Minister Andrei Grechko wrote: "The time factor has particular significance in combat readiness. During wars of the past, rather extended times were given for bringing the troops into a state of readiness. At present, the enormous speed of the [nuclear] missiles and aircraft requires that the troops be brought into a state of full combat readiness in literally a few minutes . . ." Apparently the Russians don't intend to waste a period of weeks to mobilize, during which time NATO could be doing the same thing. For the Russians to be so obliging, they would be military morons, which they're not.

Why wouldn't the Russians wish to attack first with nuclear weapons, by far the most effective weapons in their arsenal? Beats me, unless they're playing ball with the NATO strategists, the most influential of whom have been Americans. Why would they want to refrain from using weapons whose employment underlies the structure, posture, training and exercising of the Red Army?

"Nuclear weapons have made fundamental changes in military affairs. This weapon, as the most effective and powerful one, is the primary means of destroying the enemy. Its use is expected to ensure the rapid achievement of strategic results at the very start of combat actions . . ." said Marshal Pavel Rotmistrov, chief marshal of Soviet Armored Forces. As such, why would the Soviet General Staff plan to fight indecisively with conventional weapons only? They haven't hesitated to use chemical weapons in Afghanistan when they believed they were required. Why would they refrain from using nuclear weapons against their Number 1 military foe, NATO, which has a pack of similar weapons that could be used against Russian forces if they were using only conventional arms? This just doesn't hold up unless, again, we believe that the Soviets behave like military morons.

Why would the Soviet marshals allow NATO to get in the first nuclear whack against their tank forces, which the United States says would knock the stuffing out of them (especially if neutron bombs were used)? Well, maybe they will, but they sure as the blazes claim they wouldn't.

"To attain the greatest effectiveness, it is recommended that the nuclear strikes be launched at the start of the firepower preparation unexpectedly for the enemy. Preemption in launching a nuclear strike is expected to be the decisive condition for the attainment of superiority over him and the seizure and retention of the initiative," wrote Colonel A. A. Sidorenko in a book on nuclear battlefield operations that drew great acclaim from the Soviet military. So where does NATO get off by assuming the divine right of first nuclear strikes for itself? Still again, we see a contriving to make the Soviets out to have no military smarts whatsoever.

But now we get to the crux of the matter—Phase III. Assuming the Soviets have committed every possible blunder in military logic so far in the war, but doggedly plough ahead despite being whacked by our awesome neutron bombs, they now turn the other cheek and give us another chance to hit them with nuclear weapons, and still refuse to hit *us* with nuclear weapons. Suppose, however, we really let loose with the big guns, using our strategic nuclear forces against targets in the USSR. If it was one thing for the Russians to take it manfully on the chin in Europe from our tactical nuclear strikes, are they really going to sit still and let us clobber their own country? For the reasons given by Colonel Sidorenko, they claim they won't let this happen. They will preemptorily attack in an attempt to reduce possible damage to themselves. But even if, once again, they play it stupidly, waiting to be hit, it's awfully hard to believe that after being banged up by a salvo of thermonuclear weapons, they won't bang us up in return. They may be stupid, but they're not insane.

Why, unless an American President and his key advisors have lapsed into lunacy, would we want to lob thermonuclear warheads at the Soviet Union when we stand a very high probability of getting exterminated as a nation? Why would we do this ostensibly on Europe's behalf when such strikes against the Soviet homeland would have no significant effect whatsoever toward preventing the Red Army from rolling all the way across Europe?

Would we do it for no other reason than because we have pledged to our allies that we would? If so, may the Lord help us!

For all the reasons discussed above, the "no first-use" issue regarding U.S. nuclear pledges to NATO has to be as phony as a three-dollar bill. Soviet doctrine, as stated by them and officially acknowledged by us, makes it very clear that should war start in Europe, the Russians will preempt any possible first use by us and hit us with nuclear weapons before we hit them. They would be fools not to, which was observed many years ago by Henry Kissinger, who (in 1965) declared: "Regardless of what we may decide, the Soviets may introduce nuclear weapons first; in fact, if they have not lost their senses, they almost have to use nuclear weapons first." (Of course, Kissinger was a private citizen at this time. When he came into the Nixon White House, he promptly forgot about his previous nuclear profundity, fell in with the party line and, like his predecessors and successors, proceeded to give Europeans reassurances that the U.S. first-use pledge remained true and inviolate.)

What makes this far more serious in its implications for our survival is that we, the United States, know what we're up to in keeping with this NATO strategy, which was devised and pushed toward the Europeans about twenty years ago by Robert McNamara and his Whiz Kids. Our leaders in Washington aren't so misguided as to believe the Russians are as stupid as they make them out to be. In fact, our government has officially admitted that the Soviet military doctrine is actually what the Soviets claim it is.

Several years ago, while Secretary of Defense, James Schlesinger described the Soviet/Warsaw Pact capabilities as follows:

> Warsaw Pact forces, current doctrine and training indicate a readiness, however, for conducting war in Europe with theaterwide, large-scale nuclear strikes. Their large armored forces are postured to exploit these nuclear attacks with rapid, massive penetrations . . .
>
> The Warsaw Pact does not think of conventional and nuclear war as separate entities . . . Warsaw Pact strategy, doctrine and forces are still strongly oriented toward nuclear operations . . .

Harold Brown, while Defense Secretary, addressed the problem of who will make the first nuclear strike:

> The largest part of the Soviet theater nuclear capabilities is concentrated against Western Europe. This concentration, and the emphasis on Soviet military doctrine on nuclear preemption, mean that we must plan for the possibility that the Warsaw Pact rather than NATO would be the first to use nuclear weapons. Such a use might occur at the outset of a conflict or after a preliminary conventional campaign . . .

NATO strategy plans for the Russians to eschew nuclear weapons as we do—even more than we do. The Russians say they won't play ball; and U.S. intelligence apparently agrees. So why do we go on with the charade? The answer is very simple: Because we want to, and our NATO allies want us to. Neither side of the Atlantic seriously wants to contemplate using nuclear weapons. The European side doesn't even want to contemplate using conventional weapons, because it doesn't want to contemplate another war. So what's left: The Alliance, which, if war ever does start, and apparently the majority of Americans think it will, will turn itself into a suicide pact, except that our European partners seem to be in no mood to swallow the cyanide pill along with us. (Charles de Gaulle saw this coming a long time ago and took steps to pull France out of the military side of the NATO alliance. France may not be powerful enough to survive by itself, but at least it has had the good sense not to want to die with everyone else.)

All signs point to the probability that while we bang away at Russia with our hydrogen warheads and the Russians bang away at us with their hydrogen warheads, the Europeans will lay down their arms and chance their future under Soviet communism, *alive.* We'll be dead. Whether the Russians will be dead too is problematical, but at least they've been doing the proper things to try to survive: air defense, civil defense, ballistic missile defense, hardening their national political control system, etc. But in all probability, in accordance with their preemptive doctrine, at the same time they strike NATO they'll slam us with their strategic nuclear weapons to lessen the retaliating blow in case we slam them back.

We've got to get out of this mess. We've got to survive as a nation, instead of propelling ourselves toward national suicide with this matrimonial pact called NATO. The love affair, if there ever was one (and if there ever was one, we loved them; they, as they always have, went on loving themselves and exploited the hell out of our lovable nature), is over. Let's part company as good friends and let's sell them everything possible to help them help themselves to survive if they want to, including selling them nuclear weapons—plus neutron bombs. If this means violating the Nuclear Non-Proliferation Treaty, well, so be it. If the alternative to violating the treaty means that Europe can stand on its own two feet and remain free of Soviet domination, then for gosh sakes let's do it. But the time has come for us to withdraw our forces from Europe and return most of the soldiers to civilian life. It could save us a fantastic amount of money. The cost of our military contribution to NATO has now exceeded one hundred billion dollars a year.

Suppose we woke up one day to the folly of our ways in trying to defend much of the world against Soviet aggression. Suppose we then set about a drastic overhauling of our national security policy toward determining what we have to do to survive in the Nuclear Age. Were this day ever to come, what should our paramount security objective be? The answer is simple: the nuclear defense of the United States against possible nuclear attack. And how might we best implement this new policy? Again, the answer is simple: Do essentially what the Russians have been doing.

What have the Russians been doing? Just about everything. For years they have been pursuing all paths to ensure that, were they to get into a nuclear war, they would survive to a degree where they could carry on. Unlike ourselves, they have sensibly put their nuclear weapons to work to be used, if necessary, to protect their country. They claim that this is a moral imperative. They are right.

They have built up a force of offensive nuclear missiles that are superior to ours. Their missiles are designed to knock out, as much as possible, our nuclear retaliatory capability before we use it on them. And they have good reason for doing so. After all, going practically all the way back to the beginning of the Nuclear Age, we have been threatening a first strike (in line with our "first-use" nuclear pledges to allies) against them if they don't behave themselves.

They have built up the most enormous air defense system in history to cope with our nuclear bombers. They have continued to modernize this system, while we deliberately emasculated ours. There is every indication that, wherever it seems to provide greater effectiveness, they will arm their air defense weapons with nuclear warheads.

They have maintained an extensive research and development program on antiballistic missiles (ABMs). There is evidence that they have been testing these weapons disguised as air defense missiles, in violation of the ABM Treaty they signed with us in 1972. Many intelligence experts are concerned that they are producing an ABM capability that they will deploy someday soon. (The Soviets are great at breaking treaties.)

Finally, for many years they have been constructing civil defense shelters to preserve the political leadership and the industrial work force in case of nuclear war. Their propagandists may tell the Western world that nuclear war will be an unimaginable catastrophe, but their civil defense efforts to avoid this catastrophe belie their propaganda.

The Soviets have been doing all these things because they have never lost sight of the possibility that, despite all efforts to avoid it, which they have certainly been taking, nuclear war may happen anyway. On our side, though the American people have recently begun to fear that nuclear war is a distinct possibility, even during this decade, we have been doing very little toward ensuring our survival of such a war. The present administration, which gave the initial impression that it might move realistically toward ensuring survival, has now backtracked and continued with the policies of its predecessors: policies of nonsurvival that all but end our chances for defending ourselves.

In the area of offensive ballistic missiles, our efforts to replace the aging, highly vulnerable (to Soviet nuclear attack) Minuteman ICBM were a farce. Rarely has a new strategic weapons program been so poorly run as that for the MX. And while we wallowed in indecision over the MX, the "window of vulnerability" for our strategic retaliatory capability (which the President, while campaigning, worried about and promised to close as quickly as possible) opened wider and wider. If we could start all over again on trying to find a replacement for Minuteman, what would be the best way to do it?

For starters, it would be best if we were to think small—not big as we did in pushing the MX concept. With few exceptions, our experience with great big nuclear delivery systems has been that they cause more problems than they solve. We would want to scale down our sights and take a look at what prospects little missiles, exploiting advances in nuclear warhead technology, might have. I've done so and, like all nuclear weapons analysts who like their own ideas best, I will try it out on you. (I also tried it out on President-elect Ronald Reagan, who, when he became President, passed it on to the "System" in Washington, where it met the response that all outside ideas meet: Not invented here.)

The best way to get a survivable missile system is to make it mobile. We would not want to restrict the area over which it is deployed. The best way to get a politically acceptable missile system is not to deploy it where folks become aware of it and become scared to death that their neighborhood may become ground zero in a nuclear attack. (Needless to say, the MX basing scheme proposals ignored both these requirements; it wound up in a pot full of trouble.) One way to meet these needs, I think the best way, based on an idea I concocted many years ago, is to develop a very small, cheap missile, weighing less than one tenth of the MX, which can be placed in very small, cheap boats. The boats would then be sent out to sea—in the Atlantic, the Pacific and the Gulf of Mexico.

These boats, which would also be armed to defend themselves, could be camouflaged to look like fishing boats so it would be more difficult to identify them. They would meander around for several weeks, hundreds of miles offshore, and then return to shore for a crew change.

What do you think of it? Does it pass your test? If it does in principle, you ought to be real worried. Because we're talking here about thousands of nuclear missiles, the majority of them thousands of miles away from the Great Button Pusher in Washington, one or more of which may be dispatched toward Russia by some crazy skipper who wants to get credit for starting World

War III. You ought to turn this proposal down flat. It's really dangerous. But I've got an idea for getting around your objection.

There's no reason why these missiles should be deployed fully armed, ready to go. If we want to, thanks to the guys who work in our nuclear weapons laboratories, we can arrange to have the missiles disassembled during peacetime. They have to be screwed together in case of war. This can be accomplished by dividing the missile into three parts: (1) the rocket booster; (2) the reentry vehicle (which we used to call the nose cone), containing the missile guidance and control mechanisms and the nuclear warhead—without the nuclear component (i.e., fissile material) necessary for a nuclear detonation to occur; and (3) the nuclear component, i.e., a capsule of fissile material. The ground rules would be that each boat would be allowed to carry only one of these parts.

One boat could carry, say, two or three rocket boosters. Another could carry, say, five or ten reentry vehicles. Still another boat could carry, say, five or ten fissile capsules. The boat skippers would be under instructions to stay away from each other during peacetime, thereby making conspiratorial schemes *à la* Strangelove difficult. Moreover, to make even more certain that there will be no hanky-panky, the fissile capsules would be placed in containers under coded "lock and key," the code being given only in case of war. And just in case somebody tried to tamper with the container, a device could be attached that, sensing tampering, would render the capsules unusable.

The boats, of course, would be in contact with the National Command Authority (NCA), as is the case for our nuclear missile submarines. If war were to occur, or if a crisis arose which might lead to war, the NCA would tell which boats to contact other boats so that they could rendezvous and screw the missiles together.

If you like the idea, write to your congressman and tell him. I'd appreciate it. But short of that, I hope I've impressed upon you the need for the United States to have survivable strategic missiles that can be deployed outside the country, so we can get our minds away from these things and worry a little less about nuclear bombs falling on our country. If we are going to have credible nuclear weapons, we must take into account the views and fears of the American people when designing them. We haven't so far. The Pentagon has gone about this business with a callous disregard for people's feelings. And, as far as I'm concerned, they more than deserve the backlash they're finally getting these days.

In his farewell address, George Washington not only advised us to stay out of other countries' wars by not committing ourselves to fighting their wars (" 'Tis our true policy to steer clear of permanent alliances with any portion of the foreign world"), but he also advised us to protect ourselves at home "in a reasonably defensive posture." Having an ocean between ourselves and countries that might attack us, it has not been too difficult for us to protect ourselves during most of our history. But Washington, as sage as he was, hardly foresaw the Nuclear Age and intercontinental nuclear missiles.

Today, because we have viewed nuclear war in such apocalyptic terms, and decided that practically any level of nuclear attack on our soil would mean the end of everything, we have turned our backs on Washington's advice. We have deliberately emasculated our defenses. And we stand effectively naked to nuclear attack—by almost anyone. We have rationalized this technically by claiming that no perfect defense is possible (even a slightly imperfect defense would let through more nuclear warheads than we can tolerate), and morally by claiming that taking defensive measures would increase the chances of nuclear war by telling the Soviets that we would be more likely to make a first strike against them. I don't understand these arguments; in fact, I find them indefensible. What in heaven's name is wrong with trying to save lives?

Who has been blessed by such Godlike prescience that he can say that a nuclear war will be so horrible that those who survive will wish they were dead, regardless of what we might do to protect ourselves? Do these guys have access to the Soviet nuclear war plan and the nature of the Soviet nuclear stockpile to allow them to make such prophesies? You know they don't, but that doesn't stop their antics. Let me tell you about an experience with one of these guys last April in Boulder, Colorado, where I was attending a conference on world affairs.

Needless to say, the mood surrounding the conference was that the world will come to an end if the nuclear arms race isn't stopped and reversed. In that frame of mind, all sorts of nuclear war discussion panels were arranged, having such fascinating titles as: Until Hiroshima, Inventory of Weapons, Peace Game, The Nuclear Brink, Ways Out, and After World War III. I was put on several of these panels, along with a physician from Boston. This was Jonathan, who was the head of a medical organization whose membership has grown like wildfire, and which is sounding the tocsin over the horrors of nuclear war. They maintain that the medical problems will be of insuperable proportions and that there is absolutely nothing that the U.S. medical community can do to alleviate them.

During each panel that I attended with Jonathan, he would deliver a standard spiel on what would happen to U.S. cities when the Russians H-bombed them. However, the major thrust of his spiel was that the Russians would deliberately target U.S. cities—but good!

More likely than not, he would single out poor Denver (right next door to Boulder) for attack and drop (get this) seven one-megaton bombs on the city. Naturally Denver got wiped out. (Just to show his objectivity, on one occasion he put a megaton bomb dead smack in the middle of Boulder.) I'm not one for platform debating, and the first time around I let his remarks go and gave a spiel of my own. But the second time I got angry, and when he had finished wiping out Denver, I took after him.

Were the Soviets ever to make a nuclear attack on the United States, among other horrible horribles would they indeed dump seven one-megaton bombs on Denver? I doubt it. They have shown no signs of being such nuclear monsters, of wanting to wipe out the U.S. population, which would be the height of irrationality. As a matter of fact, Jonathan would have to admit that they are not irrational monsters, since his main pitch was that we have to negotiate with them to rid the world of nuclear weapons. Surely he wasn't suggesting that we could sit down with a bunch of maniacs to hammer out a disarmament treaty.

As to what the Russians have in store for us if we go to war, for many years they have been giving us a reasonable idea in the form of their official military doctrinal writings (which Jonathan apparently never bothered to read). And what they write (for their own consumption, not ours; although they make no attempt to hide any of it from us), while it hardly implies that we will receive a tap on the wrist, it does not imply that they intend to slaughter the American people. That nuclear war will be a brutal, deliberate business, they confirm. But deliberate brutality, apart from pursuing military objectives, is flatly rejected, as explained in a paper contained in *Military Thought,* the official journal of the Soviet General Staff:

> . . . if the aim of the war is just and progressive, then by no means are the classes and states waging it indifferent to the ways and means this purpose will be attained. And in this sense the principles of a just war reject senseless cruelty and violent actions not dictated by military necessity. Here, however, it must be remembered that even just wars demand sacrifices, and it is inconceivable to attain victory in them without severe, ruthless actions aimed at the decisive rout of the enemy, for such is the nature and law of armed conflict in general.

The broad purpose of waging nuclear war is explained in another paper in *Military Thought:*

> The objective is not to turn the large economic and industrial regions into a heap of ruins . . . but to deliver strikes which will destroy strategic combat means, paralyze enemy military production, making it incapable of satisfying the priority needs of the front and rear areas and sharply reduce the enemy capability to conduct strikes.

So lookie here, Jonathan, these guys don't seem at all to be nuclear Genghis Khans desirous of incinerating every U.S. city. They're out to fight a military war as effectively as possible. Sure, a lot of U.S. cities are going to get banged up, because they have factories turning out critical military goodies. But that Denver will be reduced to rubble by seven one-megaton bombs—uh-uh. But I'm not through yet. Even if the Soviets do attack key factories near or in American cities, what size bangs will be in Soviet nuclear warheads? Are they all going to be in the megaton class, whereupon the urban damage will be godawful? Not necessarily, for a number of reasons, one of them being, and you ought to know about this as a devout nuclear arms controller, that seven years ago the Soviets signed a treaty with the United States agreeing not to test warheads with megaton yields.

Long ago, in 1966, an article appeared in *Military Thought* pointing out that the Soviets had no desire to put the biggest bang possible in their warheads. As General Kruchinin explained: "Initial attention is given to the selection of those enemy targets against which nuclear means could best be used. Depending on the features of the strike targets, a selection is made of the nuclear weapons carriers . . . which could best and most rapidly execute the assigned mission with minimum expenditure of explosive power." Indeed, since that time there has been every indication that the Soviets have been moving in the direction of minimum yields, primarily by increasing their missile accuracy. The greater the accuracy, the smaller the yield required to destroy the target.

Last year U.S. Defense Secretary Caspar Weinberger stated publicly that Soviet ICBM accuracies had pulled ahead of ours. And ours were already pretty good—having a miss distance, from target, of but several hundred feet. Whereas such accuracy wouldn't exactly allow putting a bomb right down the smoke-stack, it certainly doesn't call for megaton yields to destroy an industrial target. In fact, a kiloton yield, coupled with this accuracy, would be more than sufficient to put the target out of commission, thereby doing the job at one-thousandth the bang that Jonathan, a very idealistic, genteel person, so brutally puts on American cities.

In 1976 the United States and the USSR signed the so-called Threshold Test Ban Treaty, which forbids nuclear testing above 150 kilotons of yield. Assuming that the Russians have behaved like good boys, which Jonathan will maintain has been the case, and not violated the treaty, for seven years they have been testing and probably developing strategic warheads below 150 kilotons. So we would expect that the warheads in their future strategic stockpile, if not in their present one, will have maximum yields about one-tenth the Jonathan stockpile yield. I'll grant you that a bang of 150 kilotons is awfully destructive, approximately 10 times the yield of the Hiroshima weapon. But it still is far below the megaton level. Moreover, for the reasons given above, one cannot assume that such big bangs will be used against such physically "soft" targets as industrial plants. It is far more likely that these big bangs will be used against such "hard" targets as missile silos, which are usually far away from cities.

Enough of all this fancy analysis. I just wanted to tell you,

Jonathan, that I sure wish you would tone down your horror story a bit.

What I've been trying to say here is that our fearless political leaders, our responsible physicians, our concerned scientists and many others may not be preaching the gospel when they preach nuclear holocaust. I'm not trying to say that nuclear war will be a picnic—it has to be a terrible business any way you cut it. The point is that it doesn't have to be the end of everything. That is, unless we want it to be, which may well be the case. I cannot guarantee, nor can anyone else, that nuclear war will be "survivable" (the term being essentially subjective; everyone having his own ideas on whether *he* could survive), but I will maintain that it could be. This is so especially if we try to survive—which we have yet to try to be able to do, unlike our Russian friends.

There is much that can be done toward protecting ourselves against Soviet missile and bomber attacks. (Obviously the Soviets would agree, because they're doing their best to protect themselves against similar threats.) How effective such defenses might be, nobody can predict. But there are very promising approaches that can be taken, the most important of which exploit nuclear explosives.

How many lives and how much of our material assets might be saved by such actions, I don't know. But I would claim that the amount would be considerable, if we pumped enough money into such an effort. Of course, lives are priceless and one can hardly place a dollar-value on a human being. (Look at how totally unselfish Americans can be when it comes to saving the life of someone who requires extremely expensive medical care to survive.) As for our material assets, being a good capitalist society, we do place price tags on our homes, businesses, factories and the like, and I can assure you that the cost of an ABM weapon that shoots down an incoming enemy warhead is a lot less than the cost of the property it saves. In terms of crass dollars and cents, defensive weapons, assuming they work even halfway decently, represent a real bargain value. If an ABM weapon, which might cost some millions of dollars, can save some fraction of a city, worth some billions of dollars, from being demolished, that has to be a pretty good bargain. And the ABMs do not have to be 100 percent effective to make it possible to avoid enormous levels of urban damage.

This brings up the issue of civil defense, to protect ourselves against the effects of the nuclear warheads that ABM defenses do not shoot down.

Last year the administration proposed a four-billion-dollar civil defense program and defended it with claims that it would double the number of American lives saved in a nuclear war. The Federal Emergency Management Agency, which is in charge of civil defense, stated that "the United States could survive nuclear attack and go on to recover within a relatively few years." A Pentagon official said that "everybody's going to make it if there are enough shovels to go around [to dig fallout shelters]." And, predictably, all this hit the fan.

Antinuclear organizations put up an enormous fuss. Major newspapers editorialized that we had long known that nobody can survive nuclear war, and castigated the administration for its irrresponsibility. Congressmen began to get the message and the Senate Arms Control Subcommittee hauled a senior administration official up to the Hill to explain what the hell was going on. By now the administration had seen the handwriting on the wall and the testifying official was forced to backtrack, admitting to a hostile group of senators: "We do not seek, nor do we believe that it is possible to obtain, levels of protection from the effects of all-out nuclear war that would reduce significantly the unspeakable horror of such an event." (He sounded just like Jonathan.) That statement, for the time being, pretty well put the kiss of death on getting an effective civil defense. Politics (over defense) as usual. Too bad. And in the meantime, not having the American nuclear war death wish, the Soviets continue to expand their civil defense program.

Were "all-out nuclear war" waged by the Soviets à la Jonathan (which now seems to be the U.S. government's version as well), I would have no quarrel with the official statement above that resigns us to extinction. However, for the reasons I have brought out here (in refutation of Jonathan, and the government—which almost always manages to refute its own facts when it gets into a political confrontation on nuclear weapons issues), the Soviets may not subscribe to the view that Jonathan holds of them. By no means do the Soviets necessarily subscribe to the view that waging all-out nuclear war is synonymous with all-out attacks against an enemy's population. So why don't we take into account the possibility that the Soviets may not wish to eradicate us all, and embark on a civil defense program that holds the potential for saving many millions of American lives, and which offers realistic prospects for our national survival?

If we were to add up the costs of providing our country with strategic nuclear weapons (offensive and defensive) and civil defense, they would be enormous. All things being equal, and Americans continuing to hate paying additional taxes, were there an attempt to add this financial burden to the existing defense budget, it would be rejected out of hand. The rationale for rejection, beside the fiscal pain, would be primarily that even with all these measures, we still might not be able to survive a nuclear war. Why pour all these additional billions into a cause that might turn out to be hopeless? These arguments might seem plausible enough, except for one thing: If we continue to spend almost all our money on conventional forces to hold back the Russians (about ten times more money than we spend on our nuclear forces), we will be risking a war someplace that will lead to nuclear war. This closes the circle.

If we were to give up challenging the Soviets with conventional forces everyplace else, and scrap the conventional forces for doing this, we would have more money than you can shake a stick at to fashion our nuclear defenses to protect ourselves back here. And most important, we would have enhanced our ability to avoid nuclear war. For we would clearly have presented the Soviets with a display of defensive nuclear strength that would assure them that any designs they might have for attacking us would not succeed. We would have presented them with a strategy they can respect: namely, their own strategy.

Do the Soviets have designs to wage nuclear war against us? I don't know. I'm inclined to feel that they don't, but I can't rule out the possibility that they might. Nor can most Americans rule out this possibility, which is why we have amassed a huge and still-growing stockpile of nuclear weapons. Even were the fondest hopes of the nuclear arms controllers to be realized and large reductions in nuclear missiles and bombers effected, there is no way to prove this would reduce chances for nuclear war, because changes in nuclear stockpiles would in no way entail any basic changes in human nature and the behavior of nations. Whatever incentives the Soviets might have to attack us would not be reduced by reducing nuclear stockpiles on both sides. This suggests that a better way to approach the problem is to redesign our nuclear forces to fit rational security objectives.

Such objectives should not involve building more offensive nuclear weapons, or necessarily reducing their numbers. In either case, our policy for using these weapons entails the senseless slaughter of Soviet people and the devastation of their cities. This is not only irrational, it is morally obscene. What they should involve, instead, is a refashioning of our nuclear stockpile, primarily for the purpose of defending ourselves and trying to survive if nuclear war does occur. Such a nuclear posture, it seems to me, would be difficult to attack on moral grounds. Were we to shift to such a posture, we might well find that the moral objections of many Americans who are appalled over growing stockpiles of offensive nuclear weapons would disappear. Such a shift would go a long way toward placing our policy of nuclear deterrence in a morally defensible position.

Okay, where should we be going in the world? Plainly I feel that we should be withdrawing from the military aspects of world involvement. In this sense, I've jumped ship on my past beliefs. I really have. Until recently, I spent most of my efforts trying to help make our military presence in the world effective and realistic, at least in terms that I could define as being effective and realistic. The trouble is that during most of these years, the United States and its allies had different definitions of what was effective and realistic. This placed me in the position of being a dissenter. Now I am a very angry dissenter—for all the reasons I've given previously. It is obvious to me that the United States and its allies are locked in policies that are cast in concrete. I don't think there is any realistic chance that these policies will change in time to give us the opportunity to avoid nuclear war. Thus, I favor the United States' withdrawal from its overseas commitments.

A few years ago, while I was in Paris, I received a call from an acquaintance of mine, Dick Allen. Ronald Reagan was in town and would like to meet me. I put on my best suit and hopped over to his hotel, where he greeted me in shirtsleeves. Reagan wanted to discuss nuclear strategy. So I told him essentially what I've been telling you. He was intensely interested, keeping me an hour over the appointed time. When I had finished telling him what a sorry mess we and our allies were in, and why, he told me that he had already been worried about the situation. Now he was even more worried. "Good!" I said. "You ought to be." I went on to tell him that I hoped he would become President, and I warned him of the difficulties he would have should he try to straighten out the mess. The men controlling our nuclear policies are all-powerful and pervasive, and, to date, they had managed to keep any administration from changing anything.

So Reagan, when he became President, brought in the same men, the Establishment. I watched it happen when I came aboard as a defense advisor during the campaign. Too bad. At least I think so, for all the reasons I've tried to spell out here. But it's not too late to change—to reverse our course abroad and turn to defending ourselves at home. It would be far easier to eliminate a hopeless policy than to go on trying fruitlessly to implement it. It's far simpler just to pull out, rather than to go on looking for some panacea to enable us to stay in. Whatever that panacea might be, it sure won't include the neutron bomb.

CHAPTER 9

THE NEUTRON BOMB MYTH

LET'S GO BACK TO WHERE we started: the neutron bomb and President Reagan's decision to produce it. What hath Reagan wrought? Not what I suspect he thought he did. Certainly not anything that could be useful in defending Europe, for the reasons I explained to him in Paris and here to you. In fact, deploying neutron weapons to Europe (if, miraculously, the Europeans were to allow this) would most probably only add to the huge, fantastically expensive and wasteful investment we've made so far in NATO.

There is no way these weapons could contribute significantly to NATO's defense, because NATO's defense is founded on a myth. The myth involves our belief that the Soviets will play according to NATO ground rules and not use nuclear weapons—unless we force them to do so by using them first. If they don't play by our rules and behave the way they have warned us they will, and since NATO forces do not know how to use tactical nuclear or neutron weapons to wage a ground war effectively (while the Soviets have been training for this for many years), there is no way that we can seriously defend against a Soviet invasion of Europe. This dismal situation certainly precludes any chances of our winning a war in Europe, which candidate Reagan promised the American people would be his military policy should American boys fight in another war. (He was whistling Dixie then; he'll be whistling in a graveyard, if we get into a war with the Russians.)

Were the Soviets to invade Europe (which NATO obviously thinks has to be a distinct possibility), the logical thing for them to do would be to start off by conducting surprise preemptive nuclear attacks. In other words, they'll do what their military doctrine strongly suggests they'll do. NATO's tactical nuclear weapons (to include neutron weapons, were they deployed in Europe), along with most of the rest of its military forces, are sitting ducks for such attacks. The Soviets would render NATO militarily impotent within a matter of minutes, the time it takes Soviet ballistic missiles to go from their launchers to their targets. This attack plan was also once strongly suggested by Henry Kissinger (when he was outside the government and criticizing those on the inside, which he's now doing again), when he wrote, in one of his brilliantly insightful books:*

> Considering the extreme vulnerability of the tactical nuclear establishment on the Continent and the fact that the Soviets would not attack without expecting to win [take note, Mr. President] . . . If there is large-scale aggression . . . the Soviets have every incentive to neutralize NATO's nuclear arsenal by launching an attack against it.

* *The Troubled Partnership,* Henry A. Kissinger (New York: McGraw-Hill, 1965).

Assuming the Soviets would follow their own strategy (and that suggested by Kissinger), the war against NATO would be over almost before it started. And our current neutron bombs, which are supposed to be capable of holding back the Red Army almost by themselves would be demolished along with, I'm afraid, a couple of hundred thousand American soldiers who are equally vulnerable to being destroyed in a surprise nuclear attack.

If we have to provide something in Europe to keep up the façade that we're willing to contribute to their defense, then I'd infinitely prefer having bombs over there instead of American boys who are hostage to nuclear attack. But the Europeans don't want our neutron bombs, they want our boys. Why give them what they want? Let them provide their own bombs and their own boys for their own defense, assuming they want to get serious about it. I am still every bit as concerned about Europe staying free of the Soviet yoke as I always have been. I have no desire to jump ship on them, thereby leaving them to the tender mercies of the Russians. But if they seriously want to survive, and are willing to accept nuclear weapons for their own defense (which they have to do, if for no other reason than that the Soviets have them for their offense), let's sell them the appropriate nuclear weapons for this purpose. For all the obvious reasons, neutron bombs ought to be at the top of their shopping list.

Pravda printed an article in 1981 that claimed I loved my nuclear offspring, my precious neutron bomb, more than my own flesh and blood, my son Paul. *Pravda* said: "His fatherly feelings toward the neutron bomb he created turned out to be stronger than his concern for his own son [who was in the U.S. Navy], who could come to his death if and when this new weapon is introduced into the arsenal at war."

However, when *Pravda* made its accusation, the Reagan administration had shown no signs of accepting the realities of the Nuclear Age, the Europeans had made it clear that they wanted no part of a credible realistic nuclear defense, the Soviets had pulled so far ahead of us in nuclear capabilities as to make our position pathetic, and Paul (thanks to military discipline) had matured and grown quite personable. Thus, I saw little reason at the time to push the Bomb. I had given up on defending Europe, and I wanted out. Politicians had so distorted the issue of nuclear defense for Europe, and so biased Americans and Europeans on the issue, that there was no real hope of turning the situation around in time.

For me, the neutron bomb has become a symbol of futility. The government has built up the Bomb as being a wonder weapon that can hold back hordes of Russian tanks while sparing the cities of our NATO allies. This is not true.

So where does the fusion neutron bomb fit into NATO's defense scheme? Militarily, it never has. Politically, it's been a royal pain in the neck. Morally, even though it offers the opportunity for European countries to defend themselves without devasting themselves, it has failed to interest any of them.

You'll recall that the Great Neutron Bomb debate began as a result of an article in *The Washington Post* in June 1977 that revealed what a government official had forgotten to delete from secret congressional testimony:

> The United States is about to begin production of its first nuclear battlefield weapon specifically designed to kill people through the release of neutrons rather than to destroy military installations through blast and heat.
>
> Funds to start building an "enhanced radiation" warhead for the 56-mile-range Lance missile are buried in the Energy Research and Development Administration.
>
> The new warhead is the first practical use of the so-called neutron bomb theory which government scientists have been working on for many years.

Immediately thereafter people and countries all over the world expressed their moral outrage about a weapon that "only destroys life." The neutron warhead became a symbol of infamy, of worldwide revulsion. But was the world revulsed over a fact or a myth?

In early 1978 the Chairman of the U.S. Joint Chiefs of Staff issued his annual defense posture statement to the Congress. The report discussed the Lance neutron warhead as a weapon that "provides over 30 percent of its initial energy in nuclear radiation, giving increased battlefield effectiveness while reducing the nominal collateral damage radius by almost one third." I suspect that you probably don't understand what the Chairman was trying to say (it's possible that he didn't know either, since these words were written by some junior officer on his staff), so I'll try to explain.

First of all, in pointing out that the Lance warhead gives out 30 percent of its energy in nuclear radiation, he was saying what I've said earlier: that neutron weapons give out far more instantaneous radiation than fission weapons. Thus a fission weapon has to produce far more blast than a fusion weapon to achieve the same radiation effect. (Which is why, in the nuclear jargon, neutron weapons are called "enhanced radiation" weapons.) However, we might note that this 30 percent radiation release is far less than that inherent in neutron weapons, i.e., 80 percent for a pure-fusion weapon. This gives us a clue that the Lance neutron warhead may not be the neutronic cat's pajamas. And our suspicion turns out to be justified when the Chairman also points out that the Lance warhead reduces "the nominal collateral damage radius by almost one third."

When we talk about *collateral damage* what is meant is the damage to the civil fabric: the urban areas, which we would like to avoid, if possible, in conducting nuclear attacks. When we talk about *nominal* collateral damage we are talking about the damage from a fission weapon with a yield of twenty kilotons, about the yield of the Nagasaki bomb—a very destructive bang. In fact, the Nagasaki bomb reached out more than a mile from ground zero to wreak devastation. Thus, according to the Chairman (who certainly would not want to mislead the Congress), the radius of unwanted damage from the Lance neutron warhead may be some two thirds of that resulting from a Nagasaki-sized bomb. Holy catfish!

Is this the capitalist bomb that doesn't destroy property? Is this the heralded weapon that kills people and leaves buildings intact? The answer is no, and survivors of the Nagasaki bombing would find such questions ludicrous. But this aspect never appeared in the media, because few people studied the Chairman's report. Everyone was having apoplectic fits about a neutron bomb that does not exist. What does exist is a bomb that destroys *everything*—not just the lives of enemy soldiers—and which isn't significantly different from the bombs it was supposed to replace. Isn't this the real issue?

I cannot see why so much fuss was made over the news that we were going to produce a "neutron bomb." The real neutron bomb was never more than a myth.